"The Japanese were bending over their suitcases. Then suddenly they straightened up. They were holding Kalachnikov carbines and hand grenades.

The whole place went crazy.

As the first shots ripped through the closed hall and the first grenades exploded, nobody quite realized what was happening. The noise was appalling. People started to scream. More hand grenades exploded and hurled bodies against walls, over chairs. The noise echoed and reverberated. The chaos was total. There were more screams and people were falling, kicking legs, waving arms.

The Japanese worked with horrifying efficiency . . ."

This was the massacre at Lod Airport, 1972. Just one of the horrifying triumphs of TERROR INTERNATIONAL . . .

Dennis Eisenberg and Eli Landau

Carlos:
Terror International

CORGI BOOKS
A DIVISION OF TRANSWORLD PUBLISHERS LTD

CARLOS:
TERROR INTERNATIONAL

A CORGI BOOK 0 552 10289 X

First publication in Great Britain

PRINTING HISTORY
Corgi edition published 1976

Corgi Books are published by
Transworld Publishers Ltd,
Century House, 61–63 Uxbridge Road,
Ealing, London W5 5SA
Made and printed in Great Britain by
Cox & Wyman Ltd., London, Reading and Fakenham

CONTENTS

PART ONE: MASTER AND STUDENT PRINCE

1: Boudia: The Master   12
2: Moscow: The Meeting Ground   33
3: Carlos: A True Prince   37
4: Friendship and Farewell   44

PART TWO: TERROR INTERNATIONAL

5: The Mini-skirts That Misfired   56
6: A Sceptical American   70
7: Swords Are Unsheathed   76
8: Enter Baruch Cohen   79
9: Kill or be Killed   85
10: The Return of Carlos   89
11: Blood for Blood   98

PART THREE: THE SWORD AND THE FLAME

12: Massacre at Lod Airport   104
13: A Clean Death   110
14: The Hunter   116
15: End of the Game . . . and Beginning   129
16: Exit Baruch Cohen   135
17: Assault on Dove Beach   143
18: Shadow and Master Become One   161
19: Death of the Master   166
20: A Mystery   174

PART FOUR: COMMANDO BOUDIA

21: The Shadow Takes Over   176

22: Strings and Preparations   184
23: Love and Violence   189
24: A Trade in The Hague   206
25: The Hunter Returns   222
26: Disaster at Orly   229
27: Orly Revisited   238

PART FIVE: THE PHANTOM

28: A True Friend   252
29: The Ghost of Boudia   261
30: Mukarbal is Interrogated   268
31: Death and Disappearance   275
32: Man of a Thousand Faces   280
33: The Hunt Goes On . . .   285

DENNIS EISENBERG, 46, was born in Lichtenberg in the Transvaal and came to Britain in 1954. He has been Foreign Correspondent on several newspapers, including the Herald and the Sun, and covered the Congo crisis, the Algerian war of independence and the troubles in Northern Ireland. Other assignments have taken him all over Africa and Europe. He now works as a freelance.

ELI LANDAU, 37, was born in Tel Aviv. He began his journalistic career on an army weekly and, after his military service in a crack parachute brigade, was appointed military correspondent of Ma'ariv, Israel's largest circulation newspaper. He has served as military correspondent on many fronts in recent years, reporting on the 6-day war, and the fighting around Suez in 1969–70.

Carlos:
Terror International

PART ONE:

MASTER AND STUDENT PRINCE

CHAPTER ONE

BOUDIA: THE MASTER

THE fingers touched his shoulders and he stiffened, automatically readying to spring into lethal action. Then he relaxed. He remembered where he was. He smiled and gave in to her touch, let her soft fingers stroke him.

The fingers caressed the muscles of his neck. He felt the woman's warm breath exhale gently and teasingly in his ear. The seductive fragrance of an expensive perfume excited his senses. He immediately recognized the distinctive bouquet, and his thoughts went leaping back to happier days in sophisticated society circles in Paris.

'Calèche,' he said quietly. 'You must have money, mademoiselle, to afford such a high-class perfume.'

He could afford to play this game. It was something he could enjoy. He knew he was perfectly safe right here in the heart of Moscow, at the Patrice Lumumba University. Not only were his fellow students all men and women handpicked by the Russians as reliable agents who were now being trained for their role in the terrorist international movement, but the whole campus was ringed by armed KGB men and security was tight and fool-proof. So, he played the game because he enjoyed it; he also played it because at this moment he needed it. He was a veteran of the Algerian underground terrorist movement, and for the time being he wanted to relax. She stroked his neck. He smiled quietly.

'Carlos,' she whispered. 'You are too clever for one man. Je t'aime, je t'aime, je t'aime . . .'

His name was not Carlos. It was Muhamad Boudia. Again

he had been mistaken for this man he so much wanted to meet.

The 35-year old Algerian was not alone in the room with this girl. She had come tip-toeing up to him as he sat on a low stool, talking intently to the Ghanaian, Naju George. Their conversation had not been about casual matters; rather, it was a philosophical discussion about whether or not it might have been better for Marxism if the communist revolution had first taken root in Germany, instead of Russia, during the First World War. Such discussions were commonplace in the University.

Now Muhamad Boudia smiled. He let the girl continue to stroke him. He felt the soft, piercing insistence of her breasts pressing through his cotton shirt into his back, felt a glow of anticipation as she brushed the inside of her thigh invitingly against his side.

Naju George was observing them. He was amused by the girl's mistake. Indeed, only an hour before this incident the Ghanaian had laughed as they crossed the courtyard of the University and another young man had shouted from the distance: 'Hey, Naju! Hey, Carlos! Wait for me!' The similarity between the Algerian and Carlos was amazing.

The Ghanaian smiled at Muhamad Boudia. The game had gone on long enough. Boudia smiled back and then turned to look up at the girl.

'I'm delighted,' he said.

A look of astonishment crossed the girl's face. She gazed down at Boudia and put her hand to her mouth and stammered: 'Please forgive me, monsieur, but I thought you were ...

Boudia studied her calmly. The pink flush of embarrassment now radiating from her cheeks merely enhanced her exquisite, fine-boned features. She was truly lovely. Her blouse was silk. Her faded blue jeans, obviously cut by a top-class couturier, had been designed to accentuate her superb, slender legs and full, voluptuous hips. She was certainly no poor student.

Still confused and embarrassed, the girl repeated in her native French: 'I am so sorry, monsieur. I could have sworn

13

you were Carlos. From behind you are so much alike. Even now, as I look at you, I could swear you are his double, or an older brother.'

Boudia let his eyes move slowly up and down her body, making sure that she did not miss his frankly insolent undressing of her person.

'There is no harm done, mademoiselle,' he said, smiling, speaking softly. 'Clearly you didn't mistake me for Carlos's sister.'

The girl's blush deepened and a spark of Latin anger flashed in her eyes. She was perhaps a little taller than Boudia. Her jet black hair was expertly cut, revealing the feminine grace of her throat and neck. She wore no make-up. A thin gold chain, holding a half-hidden pendant in the peeping swell of her breasts, was her only ornament.

Boudia had seen her before, in one of the study groups at the University, but only now did he realize that he was confronted with someone very special. He felt a pang of jealousy towards 'Carlos' – the man who had won the heart, and clearly much else besides, of this young French woman.

Boudia stood up. He took a challenging step towards her. He had personally killed scores of French settlers and soldiers, and he moved with the lithe grace of a killer. He stopped right before the girl and with piercing eyes arrogantly studied her face. He wanted to make her uneasy, but she had recovered her composure and she met his mocking gaze head-on.

Boudia smiled. Her eyes warned him not to take any liberties. He smiled and shrugged and moved casually away from her, quite deliberately softening his aggression and turning it into a rare charm. He knew that women were attracted to him and he possessed a self-assurance that had been gleaned from the dozens of seductions he had enjoyed in more luxurious days in Paris. So, he sat down again, and smiled, and put out both his hands.

'Don't be upset,' he said, caressing her with his eyes, with his voice. 'It's not the first time I've been taken for your Carlos.'

The girl returned his smile and blushed slightly and then

left the room. When she had gone, the Ghanaian laughed lightly.

'You know, it's extraordinary,' he said. 'When I first saw you, the other day, even *I* thought you were Carlos. You are surely a relative?'

'No,' Boudia said. 'But I would very much like to meet him. Apart from apparently looking so much like him, I've heard so much about this Carlos.

'I'm surprised you haven't met him at any of our parties,' the Ghanaian said. 'He is always the centre of attention – and the ladies fall for him like the snowflakes during one of these accursed Russian winters.'

The Ghanaian looked gloomily out of the window. Fired as he might have been by the joys of the Soviet paradise and the revolutionary fervour of spreading the message of communism throughout his native continent, he obviously was not impressed by the climate of Moscow.

'But I forget,' he said, turning again to Boudia. 'You have been here only a few days. You are sure to meet him soon. It is impossible to live here and *not* come across Carlos.'

Then, as the two men dressed in their warm coats and hats before setting off for another lecture in their crowded programme, Naju George grumbled again about the cold and snow, so different from the humid tropical heat he had known all his life.

'If only I could feel the sun on my back again . . .'

The Algerian, too, had known warmer days in his North African homeland. But he had suffered too much in recent years to let a little thing like the weather upset him. In truth, he was more than pleased to be in the Russian capital, and deeply grateful to his hosts for suddenly giving him hope again after being on the run for longer than he cared to remember. It had been months. It had been years. Years during which he had nearly starved to death; and when he had never known from day to day whether he would still be alive the following morning.

Hardship, then, was nothing new to Muhamad Boudia. He had led an extraordinary life . . .

Boudia had been born in one of the festering mud hovels of a miserably poor village at the foot of the Atlas mountains, towards the south. It was a one-room hut in which his brothers and sisters, his father and mother, even the goats and chickens, had all slept together, close to one another, during the freezing cold of winter and the scorching white blaze of the summer.

The poverty was total, the hardship beyond measure, and they spent their days scratching hopelessly at the earth and praying that food would be forthcoming. They endured side by side. The brutality of their existence, the hunger and the fatigue, made them bury themselves in cold silence, in a wary, self-protective isolation. There was little love in the hut. In the dark, one-room shack there was no private place and the needs of the flesh could not be hidden. Life was functional and coarse.

Boudia would never forget it. Such memories would flay his soul. Even years later, as a man, as an assassin, he would be tortured by the recollection of his father and mother in the bed, of his father breathing heavily, of his mother moaning and weeping, of the violent and liquid throes of their love-making, a passionless, shameful rape.

He would cover his ears and huddle close to his brothers and sisters. He would see the dark outlines of their intertwined bodies, and their cries and stifled groaning would torment him. It was a vision which haunted him all his life.

Yet Boudia was different. He was blessed with a rare intelligence. Allied to this was an ambition that would not let him rest, that would push him into seeking escape and discovering new worlds. He hated his father who beat him brutally and frequently. At the time Boudia didn't understand that his father did it out of frustration, out of ignorance and futility and blind rage, trying to conquer his own sense of hopelessness. So, Boudia hated him. No matter what the boy did, he received an almost daily dose of kickings and slaps, and he grew up with a cold sense of vengeance.

At sixteen years of age, Muhamad Boudia had been hardened. He understood violence and brutality and would willingly use it. Deciding to flee from home, he went fearlessly and quietly. He walked hundreds of miles, lived by theft and brute cunning, and finally reached the city of Algiers.

Within an incredibly short time this strange young man from the mountains that hold back the Sahara desert would become one of the most feared members of the FLN – the underground Arab nationalist movement struggling to free their country from the 'yoke of the oppressor'. But all of this still lay ahead of him as, for the moment, he nearly starved to death in the narrow, winding streets of the Casbah, which rises on the flank of the hill dominating the more modern French-built part of Algiers.

Sleeping in the shelter of broken drain-pipes, in cemeteries, in the debris of burnt-out shops, sometimes, particularly in winter, in the corner of a donkey stable, Muhamad Boudia somehow stumbled into manhood. It was a brutalizing growth, and a development deprived of love. But Boudia was smart; he had ambition and drive, and he quickly learnt to read, picked up all the local customs, and gradually affiliated himself with the Algerians of the Casbah.

By this time, the young man had learnt to live by his wits. He was cunning, courageous and ruthless. The revolt against the French was still brewing, and, drawn like a handful of iron filings to a magnet, he joined an underground cell of revolutionaries.

At first, Boudia was treated with contempt by the city-born Arabs, for he was nothing more than a peasant boy from the hinterland – the 'bled'. But Boudia was ready and eager to undertake any task, no matter how dangerous, and this soon made him one of their favourites.

Shortly after this came the stroke of luck which changed Muhamad Boudia's whole life.

He was introduced to Ben Bella, the mastermind of the Arab revolt against the French, and Ben Bella was quick to note the dedication and intelligence of Boudia despite the rags he wore.

The Moslem leader immediately took Boudia under his own wing. He treated him like a son, encouraged him to continue his education, and, as their personal relationship deepened, noted with surprise that the boy possessed astonishing acting abilities.

Under the guidance of the man he now regarded as his father, Boudia was sent to Paris, where he was not only introduced to wealthy left-wing sympathizers, but also entered the theatrical circles of the French capital. The French, particularly the women, went out of their way to help further his career – for they were anxious to demonstrate how 'liberal' they could be towards what middle-class Parisians would describe as nothing more than a 'despicable' Arab. Boudia understood this and he cunningly made use of it. And mixing in the elegant circles of actors and intellectuals, he learned to move naturally from one party to the other as though he had been born to their world.

He became an actor and was hailed as a brilliant talent. He used his histrionic ability for the conquest of society women and he used the society women for money. He learned all that he needed from the French, and he would use it against them.

Now, in the middle 1950's, the fighting in North Africa spread into the open – and Boudia rushed back to Algeria where he volunteered to take an active and dangerous role in a terrorist unit aimed at driving out the French.

It was here that Boudia displayed talents which not even the astute Ben Bella had guessed at. As quick and as lithe as an alley cat, Muhamad became a trained killer, taking to the role with an instinctive ease and showing no signs of remorse. He planted bombs in stores and cinemas, slit throats, shot and strangled, and he did it with the cold expertise that he had picked up when starving.

Also, he had grown to hate the arrogant French settlers who were quite open in labelling him and his brothers as nothing other than 'dirty' Arabs. Boudia therefore devoured the leftist teachings of Ben Bella. According to the nationalist leader, the misery and poverty of Moslems were caused by the 'greedy' and 'exploiting' French settlers. Although the *pieds-noirs* had built up farms and estates from the desert, Ben Bella said, it had only been accomplished thanks to the sweat of Arab labour. Thus the land rightfully belonged to the Arabs ...

Muhamad Boudia drank this in. He learned quickly and well. And it was in the teeming French settler quarters of Bab el Oued that he finally covered himself with glory, in the eyes of his fellow terrorists, by a particularly gruesome act of carnage.

Dressed as meat delivery men, Boudia and his gang drove up to a butcher's shop which had deliberately been picked because it was hidden from view by the curve of the narrow street and a tall stone wall opposite. They were bent on public vengeance for another act of terror carried out the day before, when a group of French settlers belonging to the OAS movement had cold-bloodedly mortared an Arab market-place, killing scores of Moslems.

Once inside the shop, the small gang of three terrorists whipped out guns from beneath their white overalls and ordered the customers to raise their hands above their heads. The men, women and children obeyed. They were then forced-marched towards the rear of the shop and into a large refrigerator unit.

Once inside, they were machine-gunned.

It was now that Boudia displayed his own particular imaginative genius as a killer. Instead of fleeing straight away, he ordered his men to undress the fifteen victims. When this was done, they went to work with the butcher's knives and axes, and it was not before another ten minutes had elapsed that the gang – with Muhamad's hands as steady as rocks on the driving wheel – drove off to safety in a nearby Arab quarter.

Twenty minutes later, when a housewife looking for the daughter she had sent to the butcher's shop started screaming hysterically in the middle of the street, a French army patrol hurried to the scene.

In charge of the patrol was a lieutenant temporarily seconded from a toughened paratroop division; but even this officer, who had been through the particularly brutal fighting against communist guerillas in Indo-China, went pale at the awful sight that greeted him.

Hanging on meat hooks in the refrigerator were the naked and hideously mutilated bodies of the fifteen men, women and children who had been murdered. They had been butchered so appallingly that it was impossible to tell which had been male and which female. They looked like carcasses of bloody beef.

The revenge of the French in the weeks and months that followed was fearful. White settlers and paratroopers murdered Arabs with their bare hands as they swept through the terrified Arab quarters. This savagery, in its turn, begat more savagery as the Moslem men and women, with blood-curdling shrieks and yells, struck back at the hated French aggressors.

The French looked long and hard for Muhamad Boudia. But always the imaginative and quick-witted assassin was well ahead of them. Exploiting to the full his remarkable talents as an actor, he changed his appearance with such frequency and speed that even when he found himself in the tightest of corners, he always managed to avoid capture.

And now Ben Bella, deciding to take the terrorist campaign into metropolitan France, picked the one-time village boy as his commander of operations in the southern part of the country. Boudia did well, his bloody reputation grew, and in time even the most seasoned terrorist operators were referring to him, simply, as *Le Chef*.

Then, in 1959, the French finally caught him.

Although they had no proof of just how important his role had been in the struggles against the white settlers and French army in Algeria, the authorities nevertheless suspected that this young man in their hands was more than he pretended to be – and was not just another Algerian working humbly in the ranks of the FLN.

Boudia refused to talk. He was tortured and humiliated. But through three years of detention and ceaseless insults his will never broke. Then, in 1962, when Charles de Gaulle signed the Evian Treaty, granting independence to Algeria, Muhamad was released and returned to his homeland as part of the deal that had been squeezed from the reluctant French authorities.

The reward for his devoted labour lay in the special status that Ben Bella now granted Muhamad. He was appointed to the management of the Algerian National Theatre, where the one-time ignorant peasant boy enjoyed the power he exercised as both leading actor and director.

But the fate of a reformed revolutionary is rarely as simple as this. If Muhamad Boudia believed that the rest of his days would be spent in the world of culture and play-acting, he was quickly disillusioned. In fact, he barely escaped with his life when, on the 20th June, 1965, Houare Boumedienne, up to that time a close friend of Ben Bella's, staged a lightning *coup d'état*.

Theoretically, this was supposed to be a bloodless revolt aimed at correcting 'revolutionary errors' – but many old scores were settled and blood ran freely that night in Algiers, Oran and countless other small towns and villages.

Again, it was only thanks to his quick wits that Muhamad Boudia escaped. His talent for disguise enabled him to slip away from his theatre and the city, knowing that he would otherwise be killed.

Boudia would have been killed because he was Ben Bella's protegé; and it was the remarkable Ben Bella – the 'midwife' of Algerian independence – that the conspirators were most keen to remove. The conspirators also knew that loyalty was a quality always deeply prized by Muhamad Boudia, and they realized that he would never turn against the man who had made him into a national hero. Besides, Boudia knew far too much about many of the new leaders' unsavoury habit, acquired during the struggle against the French, of stashing away personal fortunes in Swiss banks – money which had been contributed by Algerians for the glory of their brothers' cause in North Africa. Given this knowledge, and the fact that Ben Bella had to go, it was clear that his brilliant student, Muhamad Boudia, was also marked out for a quick death.

Boudia got out. And, as he slipped away from his native shores, disguised as a fisherman in a small boat, he vowed that one day he would avenge Ben Bella, the man who had encouraged him to rise up from anonymity and become a leader amongst men . . .

Like many a political refugee before him, the Algerian found himself in Latin America. There was some use for his talents as a terrorist in the seething politics of a continent where native-born nationalists looked up in admiration to Fidel Castro, the one man who had successfully thumbed his nose at the 'Yankee Imperialists' right on the doorstep of Havana.

One evening, early in 1969, a group of like-minded friends found themselves in a seedy Buenos Aires café owned by Jose Serphido – a regular meeting place for artists and youngsters with left-wing revolutionary sentiments. Around the heavy oak table sat three Argentinians, two Brazilians, a Cuban . . . and the Algerian known as Muhamad Boudia.

Their talk soon turned to details of the latest political developments; and they speculated fervently on how best to reach the true goal of Marxist revolution in their own particular countries.

Julio, thirty years old and born in a typical Buenos Aires slum not far from the café, was a brilliant but as yet unrecognized artist. It was he who had brought along Muhamad Boudia, after meeting him at the home of an out-of-work actress who had fallen for Boudia's good looks and charm, and who was now more than happy to share what little she had with her new lover.

It wasn't long before Boudia realized that Julio had indeed brought him into the company of men who thought very much like himself. The Cuban, in particular, struck Boudia as being a man of intelligence and shrewdness.

'Boudia belongs to the Algerian left,' Julio said, introducing his companion to the others.

It was a brief explanation, but sufficient in terms of revolutionary shorthand to explain that Muhamad was a political refugee who had come a long way – a man who was clearly on the run because of his views, and, more important, his actions.

In the ensuing conversation, the mysterious Cuban said

little. The others knew nothing of his occupation, other than that he tended to pop up, every now and then, in odd places on the South American continent. He had described himself vaguely as a trader in spices, something they disbelieved but were prudent enough not to dispute. The man called himself Zamora Ernesto, though they also doubted that this was his true identity. The assumption, justifiably, was that he held some senior status in Fidel Castro's regime.

Ernesto was, in fact, the Cuban dictator's agent in liaison with the heads of left-wing organizations across the whole of Latin America. In this role he supplied them with arms and funds, transferred from the Soviet Union to Cuba for the express purpose of spreading communist ferment throughout the whole continent.

Ernesto was now listening attentively to Muhamad Boudia, who spoke in praiseworthy Spanish and obviously knew how to present his opinions. It was clear that the guest was still seething with bitterness over the Algerian *coup d'état* that had turned him into a fugitive, and soon he was heatedly outlining his plan to assist the Algerian left by restoring Ben Bella, whom he was convinced was still alive, to power.

'If I had resources like yours,' Boudia declared passionately, banging one fist on the table, 'Algeria would be flowing with the blood of those who betrayed the true revolution.'

'Aren't you exaggerating?' the Cuban asked quietly.

Boudia turned to face Zamora Ernesto.

'Listen,' Boudia said. 'I am a veteran of underground war. I fought with the FLN. I was among those who sent the French scurrying back across the Mediterranean. I helped kick the settlers on their way. I know. I do not exaggerate.'

The Cuban simply nodded. The conversation continued. It flowed into the late hours of the night, over constantly refilled cups of coffee, as Serphido shuttled back and forth with clean ash-trays. Finally, when they got up to go, Boudia found the Cuban standing by his side.

'I was happy to make your acquaintance, amigo,' said the Cuban. 'We will certainly meet again.'

Boudia studied him carefully. The Cuban's eyes were frank. 'I never know where I'm going to be tomorrow,' Boudia said, speaking cautiously, as he had done for so long.

'Have you ever visited Cuba?' Ernesto asked.

'No,' Boudia said. 'I have never had the pleasure . . . And to be frank, my pockets are empty.'

The Cuban gripped Boudia by the arm and took him aside. 'Listen, Boudia,' he said, 'I am not a rich man, but please allow me to give you this.' A fifty-dollar bill was slipped unobtrusively into Muhamad's hand. 'I would like to meet you here again,' the Cuban said, 'but I have to be in Havana soon. However, I will be returning, and when I do, we must arrange to meet.'

Boudia took the money. He needed it desperately. He had to feign passion for the out-of-work actress in order to get anything at all. This money would help him.

'I'm grateful,' Boudia said. 'Truly, I am grateful. I don't know who you are, but I believe you really want to help me and that you are in a position to do just that. Yes, we must meet again.'

The Algerian had clearly guessed that there was more to this act of charity than met the eye; and Zamora was impressed by Boudia's quick-witted understanding of the situation.

'Things change in the world, amigo,' Zamora said. 'Wait. Things change. Just wait . . .'

Boudia knew all about that.

Since his escape from Algeria, Boudia had lived with the constant fear that Boumedienne's agents would catch up with him. For this reason he had been forced to keep on the move, travelling wearily from country to country, continent to continent. However, occasionally he returned to his beloved Paris, where he went to the theatre to quench his intellectual thirst, and where old friends would hide him and give him enough money to send him travelling again.

His life eventually became one dispiriting round of packing and unpacking, arriving and departing, travelling anonymously, watching out for his enemies, and always being wary of strangers. For indeed, Muhamad Boudia knew, better than most men, how easily a determined adversary can track his quarry through unsuspecting friends and loose talk ...

Since his name still carried a magical ring to it in his homeland, he managed to keep close ties with old comrades who had remained behind in Algeria. From them he learned that there were mounting rumours of a developing underground army; and it was this possibility, burning through him each night, that nourished him through the years of debilitating inactivity.

He dreamed frequently of his homeland. The dreams pained him and nurtured him. He often thought of a Japanese song, learned from a young actress in Paris, that perfectly summed up the way he felt in his heart:

> *Peace is bought with blood*
> *Blood is given by the nation*
> *Lucky is the nation*
> *Whose sons have blood*

Boudia brooded much. An objective demands sacrifice and he knew that he was willing to make any sacrifice for the freedom of his country. Ben Bella was his true leader while Boumedienne was no more than a miserable lackey of the capitalist world. Boumedienne had to be destroyed and Boudia wanted to do it – and he thought of this constantly as he lay with his actress, conscious of his dependence, of his deceit and feigned passion, wanting desperately to free himself from her embrace, from her clutches, to regain his freedom and pride, to work for the cause.

His ambitions were political; his fears were purely sexual. He could manipulate women, and use them for his own ends, but finally such relationships tortured him.

Often, as he lay next to the ageing actress, her face in the darkness reflecting pleasured contentment, he would stay on his back and stare up at the ceiling and try desperately to avoid memories of his childhood. Yet despite all his efforts, despite his dreams of revolution, the nights in his parents' hut would come flooding back to him in minute and haunting detail. At such times he had no choice – he would become a child again – he would close his eyes tight and cover his ears with his hands, trying hopelessly to shut out all the torturing memories that had been rekindled by the proximity, by the heavy breathing and the sweat, of the ageing woman who now lay beside him.

He was paying his dues.

For many years the Russians had worked hard at plucking some fruit from their costly investment in Castro's Cuba. Towards the end of 1975 they were handsomely rewarded when Havana agreed to send troops to Angola as part of Moscow's plan to spread communism on the dark continent.

The earlier effort of the Russians to win a toe-hold of consequence in Africa had foundered during the days of Patrice Lumumba when their former Congo colony was granted independence by the Belgians. The tall and slender Negro demagogue who seized power in Leopoldville – now Kinshasa – had been willing enough to follow the bidding of his Russian masters, particularly as they backed their wishes with a gift of gold into a secret Swiss bank account. But as the Soviet Ambassador there dryly observed, when President Mobutu expelled him and his horde of advisers: 'These people are not yet ready even for communism.' The lesson the diplomat preached after getting back to Moscow was simply this: 'The only way to win a backward African territory is to ensure that you have soldiers there who are trained, efficient and properly orientated politically.' The result of this was eventually to be seen in the airlifting of Cuban troops to Angola – troops highly skilled in guerrilla warfare and also imbued with communist ideology.

However, all of this still lay ahead, for it was still 1969 and KGB headquarters in Moscow were working on another ambitious project: that of uniting all the terrorist organizations which had risen in Europe and Latin America.

For here, among the men of violence, the sharp-witted Kremlin planners had spotted an ideal, ready-made weapon which could act as a short-cut to achieving their long-term aim of world-wide domination.

But the KGB agents hit a snag. The ranks of the terrorist movements contained many men who were brave with their tongues, but somehow lost their nerve when action was needed. The groups were also split by narrow ideological rifts and personal jealousies; they often fought each other and waged bitter war between themselves, something that was particularly noticeable in the Palestinian terrorist movement.

Then there was the problem of motivation. Not all terrorists were communist sympathizers, and many refused to take orders from Moscow – even though they accepted Russian arms and money. Some actually regarded the Russians as 'reactionaries' and called themselves Maoists or anarchists.

So there was a sudden flurry of interest when glowing reports about a certain Muhamad Boudia reached Moscow from their reliable and shrewd operator in Havana – the Cuban who worked under the cover-name of Zamora Ernesto.

As the Algerian was left to kick his heels in Buenos Aires – to eke out his 'advance' of fifty dollars without letting his actress lover know about it – the KGB carefully checked the past record of the terrorist with their agents in Paris and Algiers.

The results of their investigations fulfilled their fondest hopes. The Algerian could not have been better suited to their cause; he was ideal cannon-fodder for their Terror International blueprint – a man who was a proved and ruthless urban guerrilla, and was also motivated by genuine Marxist thinking.

Thus, two weeks after the Cuban's chance meeting with Muhamad Boudia in a Buenos Aires café, a special courier brought instructions to the Soviet staff in Havana:

'Do everything possible to help Muhamad Boudia and bring him to Moscow if he sounds genuinely interested.'

The process had begun.

Within hours, Zamora Ernesto was winging his way back to Buenos Aires and, as he had anticipated, found the Algerian terrorist waiting expectantly at Serphido's café. The Russian-trained Cuban knew that there must be no great display of enthusiasm on his part, no indication of the intense curiosity expressed by the KGB, so for the first hour or two his conversation was non-committal, a series of vague generalities about communism and politics.

However, Boudia was no fool. He, too, could be patient. It was something he had learnt the hard way and would need in the future. He asked no questions. He displayed no curiosity. He knew that the Cuban had come for a specific purpose, but he didn't want to force him into speaking. They acted like old friends.

Finally, at the suggestion of Zamora, the two men strolled through the teeming streets, and Zamora, almost as an afterthought, turned to his companion.

'I've given it a lot of thought,' he said. 'I can help you. But you will have to come and join me in Havana.'

'I thank you,' Boudia said, not wanting to press it any further. 'In my situation, I appreciate any gesture. I'm more than willing to do as you say.'

'You will meet other men there,' Zamora said. 'Men with means and goodwill. Men who hold opinions similiar to your own.'

'I said I was prepared,' Boudia said.

'All right. You will hear from me.'

As they shook hands, Boudia felt a crisp note being pressed into his palm. This time it was a hundred dollar bill.

Boudia felt elated. His luck was changing at last. He could feel it as clearly as the breeze now wafting in from the sea.

Now, absolutely certain that the Cuban would not let him down, Boudia walked out of the actress's life. He had not the faintest idea of what was in store for him – nor what price he would have to pay – but he sensed that it was something important and he knew he could wait for it.

This time, the wait was only six days. On the seventh, an unknown messenger brought an envelope. The envelope contained money and, more important, a one-way ticket to Havana.

At 8.30 the next morning, the Algerian took off on the first leg of a long journey that would change his life completely.

The man introducing himself to Boudia was tall, with straight blond hair and blue eyes. The meeting took place in a room at the Soviet Embassy in Havana after the Cuban, Zamora Ernesto, had met Muhamad at the airport and taken him directly there in a chauffeur driven car.

'My name is Vladimir Nishitz,' the man said. 'My friends call me Valodia. Please do me the honour of doing the same.'

Boudia guessed immediately that this was not the man's true name, but this didn't stop him from grasping the man's hand warmly. He was grateful to be here.

'I have few real friends,' Boudia said with a smile. 'So I'm happy to widen the circle.'

The Russian returned the smile. He radiated goodwill and warmth. Yet the eyes, Boudia noticed, were cool and calculating.

They sat for a while sipping coffee and eating sandwiches, chatting about the world in general. Then gradually Valodia shifted the conversation in the direction he was aiming at.

'We know the part you played in achieving Algeria's independence. It's a great privilege for me to meet one of the select few who, like yourself, succeeded in driving out the foreign oppressor.'

Valodia then gently prodded his guest into talking about that period of his life. At first, Boudia was hesitant – years had passed since those bloody days when he had been king of the streets of Algiers – but, as he relaxed, the lucid tongue of the former terrorist wove the full story of his glories. He named names, places and dates – deliberately so – for he had guessed, correctly, that a hidden tape-recorder was taking everything down. Meanwhile, his Russian companion listened in silence, sometimes seriously, sometimes with a slight smile, but never taking his eyes off Boudia.

The session was cut short at 11.00 a.m.

'Interesting,' Valodia said. 'Very interesting. I'm happy to have got the story from a first-hand source. I always did want to hear exactly what happened from a man who was there.'

But Boudia was uneasy. This wasn't quite what he had expected. Zamora had held out the hope that the Russians would help him – but this ... a pleasant chat, simply to satisfy the curiosity of a man sitting in the Soviet Embassy in Havana ... Was *this* the only reason he had been brought all the way to Cuba?

When they said their farewells, the Russian didn't even hint at another meeting. This disturbed Boudia even more. By now he had worked himself up into a state of mind where he was willing to do anything for his new friends, to serve them faithfully, to be a slave to their desires, just for the chance of killing his hated enemy Boumedienne. The Russian's silence on the matter was therefore something to worry about.

Leaving the building with Ernesto, the Algerian gave vent to his troubled thoughts. The Cuban listened patiently, sympathetically.

'Please understand,' the Cuban said. 'The Russians are not like us. We have a hot temperament, but they are different. You don't know how difficult it is even for us Cubans ...' He stopped, as if realizing that he was being indiscreet; but clearly Boudia had not been the first man from the lands of the sun to take a dislike to the Soviet comrades. 'You'll just have to wait,' he said.

So, Boudia sat in his hotel and waited. Indeed, he didn't really have too much choice. However, he had no reason to complain about the way he was being treated in Cuba, as in fact he was given VIP service. Zamora drove him everywhere, showing him Castro's achievements. He discussed them with passion and pride; and Boudia knew he was dedicated.

'We have been through some bad years, but it was worth it,' Zamora said. 'Castro was right. A nation that truly believes in its objectives has to know that the path won't be strewn with roses. First you have to get past the thorns. Patience and wisdom belong together, and dedication to purpose is the father of both.'

Shortly after the first appointment, Zamora took Muhamad for another visit to the Russian Embassy. Again, after a long talk with Valodia, there was no result. The Russian was polite, but utterly non-committal.

By now, Boudia was growing desperate. Later he would learn to appreciate that planting the seed of uncertainty in the mind of the man they wanted to manipulate and control was a basic part of Soviet tactics, but for the moment he simply fell for the trick. He grew worried and depressed.

This game of nerves continued for ten days, but finally an unexpected invitation to dinner at the Embassy was extended to Boudia.

It was a sumptuous meal. Valodia had obviously taken immense pains to ensure the right atmosphere of relaxed goodwill, but it was with the greatest difficulty that the Algerian retained his composure. He knew that whatever was being offered would be offered tonight, but he didn't know just what it might be. His heart was pounding furiously, but he tried to look calm. His face, an actor's mask, was convivial and amusing, concealing his doubts and confusion.

Finally, Valodia wiped the last pineapple juice from his lips – the absence of alcohol was in deference to his Moslem guest – turned to Boudia and spoke.

'Boudia, we intend to help you,' he said. 'Some of our people are interested in getting to know you personally. It will mean a trip to Moscow. If you find a common tongue with them – and I do believe you will – you will be expected to stay a while in the Soviet Union. However, I think we can leave the details until you get there.'

Boudia relaxed. A great warmth flowed through him. He was smiling as he was shown to his chauffeur-driven limousine and taken through the bright lights of Cuba. A new world was beginning.

What Boudia did not guess at this stage was just how thoroughly every word uttered in the Embassy during his visits, right down to the small talk at the dinner, had been tape-recorded and then analyzed by a team of experts in the KGB headquarters. Nor did he realize just how impressed the Russians were.

They had discovered that Muhamad Boudia had not been boasting about his exploits. Every claim he had made of actions taken against the French and the white settlers in his homeland had proved to be accurate. If anything, the Algerian had been a little modest in that he had omitted some of his more dramatic deeds, like the butcher-shop massacre. It was all down in Boudia's dossier, however – now a thick folder containing not only his life-story, but the Russian experts' summing up of his personality and character, his almost limitless potential as an agent for communistic expansionist aims.

Little wonder that the KGB were dazzled by this prize tool that had fallen almost by chance into their hands . . .

CHAPTER TWO

MOSCOW: THE MEETING GROUND

Moscow greeted Muhamad Boudia with the harsh winds of a severe winter storm. It was below freezing as the Algerian stepped on to the airport tarmac on the outskirts of the Russian capital; but as if to compensate for the brutal climate, he was greeted by his new comrades with a glowing and almost overwhelming warmth.

A brand new fur coat, a whole wardrobe of thick clothing, and a generous supply of money were all pressed on to the by now bemused Algerian; and the large black Russian-built car, which transported him to the city, was clearly reserved for VIPs – otherwise, why the obsequious behaviour of customs and other minor officials as two rather important hosts whisked the newcomer through passport formalities?

As in Havana, Boudia found himself facing a long round of meetings with senior officials whose real identity and affiliation he was never told. Still, he had no need to question the possibility that these men were the ones who would decide his destiny. Meanwhile, there were names, and more names: Leon Ahimatov, Alexander Ghushevitz, Nikita Starhkhin and many others. After a while, since they were obviously fictitious names, Boudia ceased memorizing them.

At the end of this initial period, after many exhausting sessions and interrogations, some of which were clearly open police investigations, the Soviets were ready to make decisions. They were prepared to help Boudia build an underground in Algeria – on two conditions (or requests, as they tactfully put it). The first was that he must spend some time in Patrice Lumumba University. As for the second ... well, that would come later.

There was only one black mark against Boudia. His Russian hosts had the feeling that the Algerian's professed communist beliefs were not altogether genuinely felt. There was the suspicion that when it came to his innermost thoughts, Muhamad was telling the interrogators only what he felt they wanted to hear. About his patriotism they had no doubts; but a truly dedicated communist ...?

The KGB men were a little uneasy, but the situation was not altogether new to them. They were particularly wary when dealing with Arabs; they knew that men like Boudia could quite easily turn against the Marxist hand that fed them and revert to their Moslem teachings, becoming in the process fanatical Arab nationalist terrorists rather than true communists willing to serve Moscow blindly. Therefore, they were worried, but not too much: the training and brainwashing, which still lay ahead at Patrice Lumumba University, would help overcome this common problem.

Innocent of this, the Algerian could not help smiling as he was driven into the grounds of Patrice Lumumba University, clearly a prize pupil about to be enrolled in a very special centre of learning. For a peasant boy who had taught himself to read and write, and who had never had a day's formal schooling in his life, there was a certain irony in finding himself a 'student' at such an advanced centre of learning.

But then, the Lumumba University was not like any other university in Russia – nor in any Western country for that matter.

Named after the martyred Congolese leader, the University was designed to give prospective leaders of revolutionary movements in Africa, Latin America, the Middle East and Europe a thorough grounding in Marxist ideology and, in addition, practical training in how to operate effectively as guerrillas or terrorists.

In short, the hundreds of students, all carefully hand-picked for their willingness to become freedom fighters, were methodically brainwashed into accepting without question the fundamentals of the Soviet expansionist policy.

To help this strange assortment of Asiatics, Europeans, Arabs and South Americans settle down in their unfamiliar surroundings, the Russians provided the foreign students with the most lavish of facilities – facilities which would have made ordinary Russian youths green with envy. Social clubs were provided, parties were encouraged, and in the dormitory wings the pace and style of life differed little from the free-and-easy atmosphere that prevailed in the 'decadent' Western world.

Ordinary Russians were discouraged from mixing with the foreigners; and only the most politically reliable native students ever had an opportunity of attending the varied social events which Boudia and his colleagues were encouraged to organize.

Almost from the first, Boudia realized that the University was designed to test a candidate's fitness to serve KGB purposes and the policies of the Soviet Union. Thus he knew what was expected of him, and he used his considerable talents to convey the image of a man who saw his future only under communist patronage.

But if Boudia felt he was in command of the situation, he underestimated the skill of the lecturers in slyly colouring all his thoughts and previous convictions with a layer of Marxism. Subtly, and without his knowledge, the Algerian's personal beliefs were being aligned to those of his hosts; Boudia was being brainwashed, gently and persuasively, and the results were unobtrusively devastating.

The cares of a man who had been on the run for so many years drifted away from Boudia's shoulders. Gone was the daily battle to keep body and soul together; gone were the fears that the assassin lay in wait just around the corner. Instead, everything was taken care of; all his material needs were provided for by the Russians. The food was good, the social life was colourful, and there were enough girls on the course to satisfy other physical needs.

Despite the hardship of his previous life, Boudia had retained his youthful good looks and sexual appetite. Added to this, the layer of charm which had been moulded to his personality during his days in Paris now proved its worth as he found many willing female partners to keep him company at night. And no longer dependent on them, no longer hunted by the assassins, he could go to their bodies in peace, free from old memories . . .

CHAPTER THREE

CARLOS: A TRUE PRINCE

CARLOS'S strong fingers strummed over the guitar strings, sometimes caressing them gently, sometimes striking them with controlled ferocity, the total effect, no matter what particular mood took him, devastating the admirers who crowded around the room of Naju George.

True to his word, the Ghanaian had ensured that there would be a good turnout for the party he had organized that night – not a difficult thing to arrange since Carlos was the prize guest and the most popular young man in the University.

Carlos sang in Spanish. He then sang in Russian. When the applause had died down, he sang in English and French, love songs, painful songs, romantic and abstract, the words far removed from the things they were learning in this unique school for guerrillas and terrorists. His fellow students adored him.

Boudia, who was in a cramped corner between a chest of drawers and an occupied armchair, had watched with great interest the arrival of the young man he had heard so much about. Rumour had it that Carlos was unsurpassable at everything he tackled – an outstanding sportsman, intellectually brilliant, irresistible to man and woman alike – so Boudia, understandably, was intrigued. Also, he had been mistaken for Carlos so many times, he now wanted to see what the resemblance was – if indeed there was any.

Carlos had arrived seconds before midnight, his dark eyes shining, the guitar draped casually over his shoulder. His casual entrance, however, was a charade. Indeed, he had

entered the room with such studied ease that even Boudia –
himself a master of the dramatic effect – was visibly impressed and amused.

Carlos had entered with two ladies. The first was
Mademoiselle Calèche – as Boudia had now labelled her –
the girl who had mistaken him for Carlos in the study, and
the second was an adoring, buxom blonde. Shorter and less
attractive than the lovely French girl – now dressed in a
deceptively simple peasant-style blouse and full skirt – the
other girl turned out to be German. To the keen eyes of
Boudia, she was obviously a political animal, one who, in
bed, was more likely to get involved in a deep discussion of
Marxism rather than relax and simply enjoy the pleasures of
sex. Boudia much preferred the exquisite Mademoiselle
Calèche.

There was no doubt that Carlos was popular. Perched on
a table, the guitar in his hands, his handsome features
wreathed in a cloud of cigarette smoke, he radiated that
special look of youthful sincerity that captivates even the
most suspicious strangers. He played the guitar. His voice
was smooth and caressing. The girls crowded around him
and gazed up with star-struck, adoring eyes.

As Boudia carefully studied this newcomer to the party,
he quickly got over the petty jealousy he had felt when the
French girl had caressed the back of his neck in the mistaken
belief that it was Carlos she was teasing. For indeed, the
Algerian had to admit that there *was* a striking resemblance
between himself and the popular young man. In particular,
there was something oddly familiar about the shoulders,
something that the Algerian tried to analyse.

Then, when he caught Carlos in an unguarded moment, he
realized what it was. For the expression which flitted briefly
over the face of the Latin American told the Algerian that
this was no innocent youngster. In that passing careless
moment a look of hardness, of steel, had appeared on the
guitarist's youthful features – a look which told Boudia that
here was a man much older than his years, a man who had
known suffering and danger – a man who had the killer
instinct.

38

The shoulders told the same story. Like Boudia's own, they sloped inwards, they slumped; they were the shoulders of a man who had been burdened with much responsibility and care. Also, Carlos's thick neck and heavy, muscular arms were physical traits reflected in Boudia. Little wonder that the two men had been mistaken for each other so often.

Boudia made no attempt to talk to Carlos, to seek out his company as did everybody else in the room, both male and female, during the next few hours. Instead, he simply sat back in his corner and watched the youth revel in his own popularity.

Obviously his real name was not Carlos. Everybody at the University went by an assumed name. Sooner or later they would all have to leave their protected world in Moscow and become members of some underground movement; therefore, in their mutual self-interest, it was best that no-one knew the true names of even those who became close friends or lovers.

Boudia, himself, was called 'Pierre Guillet'.

When Carlos had tired of singing he laid down his guitar, but his audience, who were enamoured of his talents as a story-teller, begged him to tell them another.

'Stories?' Carlos said, laughing self-effacingly. 'Why *me*?'

'Yes, Carlos! A story! Tell us a story!'

Carlos, smiling, deliberately waited for the pleading to build up to a crescendo. It was obvious to Boudia that behind the façade of humility Carlos relished this reputation as a skilled raconteur, had the arrogance and the vanity of all natural performers, and was most vibrant when facing an attentive audience.

Throwing his arm around the German blonde, Carlos pulled her closer to him. She offered no resistance as he slid his hand between her breasts and exclaimed: 'One needs to feel the softness of a woman for the mind to relax!' Then, when Mademoiselle Calèche put on a hurt expression, Carlos turned from the blonde and ran his hand along Calèche's thigh, finally letting it rest in her lap. 'Never mind,' he said mockingly. 'I am yours, also.' Her lips trembled. Her eyes shone with suppressed excitement. She tried hard to stay calm and not squirm under the hand of her lover. The hand rested, quite deliberately within an inch of her most intimate sexual zone.

Everyone could see the little game being played by Carlos as he kept both women delicately balanced between longing and the promise of fulfilment. Then, as Boudia switched his attention from the face of the French girl to that of Carlos, he caught the look of cool inquiry aimed in his own direction.

With practised self-assurance, the North African looked straight back. Friendliness mixed with caution – but none of the adulation which was on the faces of the others in the room – formed the mask with which he met Carlos's steady gaze.

They had acknowledged one another.

Suddenly, Carlos began to talk. He did it with one arm wrapped around the German girl, the other hand in the lap of the French girl. Neither seemed to hear a word he said as they sat with closed eyes. Sure of himself, he smiled at the people around him, slyly seducing them. His voice was soft. It was light as a feather. It floated over them and around them and enfolded them with the actor's pure guile.

'Yesterday,' he said, 'I found out where I came from. I got hold of a precious document, written in gold letters, which is kept in my family and handed down from generation to generation, each time the head of the family passes away. I am the oldest son. My father died years ago. But mysteriously, the ancient document had vanished.'

Carlos had switched to English – the common language amongst the students when they relaxed in each other's company – and Boudia now tried to analyse the voice, tried to ascertain just where in Latin America Carlos had picked up his English and Spanish. At first, he couldn't find an answer, but eventually it came to him. Carlos spoke English with that typical accent and inflexion which sprang from the voice of an Arab born in the Middle East. The accent was faint, most certainly, but it was there nevertheless.

'Two weeks ago,' Carlos continued, 'the document was found in an old casket in the family palace near Mexico

City. Some kind people sent it to me and at long last I could know of my origins. So now I tell you simply: Carlos is a child of the sun.'

He smiled pensively. He caressed the girls beside him. The girls sat there, silent, motionless, their cheeks glowing with sexual excitement.

'I discovered that my roots are in the Aztec royal family,' he continued, building one myth upon the other. 'The ones who founded Tenochtitlan, their capital city of Lake Texcoco.'

Boudia studied the voice. He was tracing it back to its source. It was possible that Carlos *had* been born in South America – he might simply have learnt his English in the Middle East – but as Boudia listened more attentively, he became increasingly certain that Carlos was no Latin American, but had in fact been born in the Middle East. There was no mistaking that distinctive guttural sound that had since, through careful training, been disguised. He and Carlos were brothers . . .

'So you see,' Carlos concluded, smiling triumphantly at his audience, 'I am a prince. A true prince of the sun. And, what is more, a prince descended from the Sun King himself. All hail! All hail Carlos!'

The audience roared. Such nonsense entranced them. They applauded and shouted for more, but Carlos bowed and relaxed. Boudia, still crouched in his corner, smiled with amusement.

Later, when Boudia was formally introduced to Carlos, the story-teller said with mock simplicity:

'Welcome to our happy band!'

Boudia bowed slightly and smiled. 'A beautiful story,' he said. 'But who are you really? Carlos is such a humble name for a man of such regal distinction.'

'There are many called Carlos,' the young man said, unperturbed. 'So why not me?' He was sipping from a glass of beer. He looked closely at Boudia. He smiled and abruptly lowered his voice and put his head close to Boudia. 'You are a clever man,' he said. 'I saw that immediately. You sat in your corner and you pretended to be nobody, but I did not for one minute believe it.' He moved even closer. 'Men like us,' he said. 'We can understand each other. We do not need words or simple proof. However, I offer it.' With a sudden gesture, he pulled a passport from a pocket sewn on to the thigh of his jeans. He passed it to Boudia and ordered him to study it.

'Carlos Ilich Ramirez Sanchez,' Boudia read.

'Son of Doña Elba Sanchez of Caracas, Venezuela,' Carlos recited with some pride, as Boudia handed him back the passport. 'Born on the 12th of October, 1949.'

'How useful to have a name like Ilich,' Boudia said slyly. 'Who could have better credentials in Moscow than a man named after the great Lenin?'

Carlos refused to be flustered. 'My father was a communist,' he said. 'I was weaned on red milk. Because of their fervent admiration for the great Marxist teacher, my parents gave me one of his names. My two brothers, likewise, were given other of his names – Vladimir and Lenin. In fact, we were always envious of the brother called Lenin. Why had he been favoured over us? Yes, it is true. We felt that our parents were showering praise on him.'

Boudia could detect no irony in Carlos's voice; and clearly the young man was not stupid. A joke of this nature would not have gone down well with the rather humourless Russian supervisors and the spies that they had in this room. No, Carlos seemed sincere. Anyone overhearing would have to conclude that his faith in communism was untarnished by cynicism.

With a sudden, graceful movement, Carlos unslung the guitar and threw it into Boudia's hands.

'Play!' he exclaimed. 'You are too strong, too hard for your own good. You must learn to relax! Enjoy yourself! The music will help you!'

The Algerian was surprised. Not for years had he held this instrument in his hands; and very few of his friends even knew of his skill with the guitar. The fact that Carlos had guessed it now amazed him.

Boudia began to play, hesitantly at first, then, as he grew confident, with a flourish. Carlos watched him. He had the eyes of a hunter. He was studying every move, every expression on the face of the Algerian. Boudia understood. He was being assessed. He didn't mind and he continued to play and the music released him.

A few minutes later, when he had finished playing, he put the guitar down and listened to Carlos.

'You are good,' Carlos said. 'You can play as well as me. I wonder if you are as good in other things.' Carlos smiled, but his eyes were alert. 'Tell me, amigo,' he said, 'what else can you match me in?'

Boudia turned the question aside with a smile, but he knew what the younger man meant. He, Muhamad Boudia, had become too jaded, too hard, too calculating ever to relax. His years as a political refugee had taken a heavy toll, had exacted more than he had previously imagined. He needed to loosen up again, to return to the old ways, to go back to being the colourful Muhamad Boudia, the youngster with the thousand faces, the King of the Casbah, the man who had loved and fought and conquered in the scorched, white-washed streets of Algiers. He had to rebuild himself.

The mysterious young Carlos, who now stood so confidently in front of him, had just taught him a valuable lesson – a lesson he had to take note of before it was too late ...

CHAPTER FOUR

FRIENDSHIP AND FAREWELL

BOUDIA felt that he was growing wings as the days passed. He began to laugh aloud for the first time in years. He felt healthy and bright and energetic. And for the first time he felt that he was really enjoying himself, even during the tedious lectures on Marxist ideology, and most particularly during the demanding military training sessions.

In the third week the students were split up into teams of ten, and Carlos and Boudia were paired up together in the same unit.

Their initial instruction concerned the theoretical studies of Marxist ideology, and during it Carlos's attention frequently wandered. In truth, he grasped new ideas remarkably quickly; he had a photographic memory that absorbed whole pages of text at a glance – and it seemed to Boudia that this was the cause of the apparent boredom which Carlos scarcely bothered to hide from the instructors.

For himself, Boudia had been taught patience and discretion in a very hard school – that of violence and subterfuge – and he was therefore at pains to demonstrate to the Russians that he knew every bit of theory by heart. Indeed, if this was going to be one long game of chess, then the Algerian knew that he must let his instructors believe anything they wanted to believe of him. Thus, it surprised nobody when Boudia was the student who finished at the top of the theoretical exams.

Carlos, however, was put out.

'I will finish number one in the operational projects,' he said to Boudia. '*Then* we shall see who is master!'

44

The challenge was good-humoured, a mockery devoid of malice, because Carlos, in the course of the past few weeks, had come to like and respect the Algerian. The two men were quickly heading towards a state of true friendship – indeed, so much so that the impulsive Carlos had pushed Mademoiselle Calèche into Boudia's bed.

At first the French girl had been unwilling; but then, with total ruthlessness, Carlos had led her to understand that unless she was 'nice' to 'Pierre Guillet' she would never be welcomed back to his own bed. Sullenly, she gave in.

The French girl's reluctance had evaporated somewhat when she experienced the expert caresses of Muhamad Boudia. He was, after all, a professional gigolo who had used more than one lady for the cause. Boudia was practised. He was coldly methodical. He could play a woman's body like a lute; he could turn it to fire and ice. And so Mademoiselle Calèche, once reluctant, now eager, started flitting with little restraint between the two men.

Neither discussed her with the other. Neither discussed the other with her. The three-way affair was an unstated, clandestine gift. All parties were satisfied.

Meanwhile Carlos was demonstrating that he could live up to his boast as a man of action.

His operational performance was superlative. He drew praise from the dour instructors for his skill in fire-arms, bomb-laying, code-breaking and all other fields of guerrilla operations. He outclassed the rest of the team – with one stunning exception. For try as he might, he could not quite surpass the tough and highly talented 'Pierre Guillet'.

Both were quick to realize that the other had seen action in real life, had probably killed, and had most certainly faced danger and death. But Carlos, mistakenly, had assumed that his own lightning reflexes would better those of the older Algerian. In this he was very wrong.

Whether it was in summing up a tricky operational situation, handling an explosive charge or pushing the body to its physical limits, the Algerian, without even appearing to try particularly hard, matched every skill that Carlos

45

demonstrated. So much so that one evening, letting his mask slip for a moment, Carlos told him frankly:

'I don't know who you are, but I admire you. And, to be honest, I would hate to have to face you as an enemy.'

'It's mutual,' Boudia said. 'When we fight, I hope we stay on the same side.'

The friendship deepened. It was strange and fulfilling. It was strengthened by a mutual respect that was based on pure challenge. Each tried to beat the other. They usually came to a draw. And as both could only feel for an equal, they felt warmth for each other.

The competition continued.

Carlos, above all, was a superlative crack-shot and so he was convinced that this was the one activity in which he could outclass the Algerian – and indeed, any other living marksman. As it was, he soon had the chance to test his theory – for at the end of the fourth week they began training in the use of light arms.

On the range, the apprentice terrorists were given only two types of pistol: a Beretta and a short-barrel revolver inaccurate beyond fifteen yards. As an initial test of skill, each pupil was asked to fire four rapid shots at a target placed fifteen yards away. Few succeeded in getting even one bullet in the centre; but Carlos scored three consecutive bullseyes and placed the fourth slightly off-centre.

He threw a self-satisfied smile at the Algerian.

Boudia smiled back. The gun was lying on a wooden shelf. He picked it up and looked at the target, and all attention focussed on him. Indeed, even the Russian instructor, who had sensed the rivalry between his two prize pupils, looked on in fascinated silence.

Serenely, Boudia looked across at the target. He weighed the revolver. He closed his left eye. His mind went back to a day in Algeria when he lay in ambush for a French patrol, knowing that if he missed the first shot there would be no second chance. Then, in one swift movement, almost too quick for the eye to follow, he lifted the revolver and fired at the target. Four shots rang out.

Seconds later, the whole group had followed the instructor to the target area where they gazed in astonishment at the results.

There was only one hole; it was dead centre.

The admiration that Carlos felt for this superb display of professionalism erased any trace of resentment or envy. He turned to his friend and put his arms around him and hugged him.

'You have the hand of a true artist!' he exclaimed. 'I bow down in admiration!'

The training continued. It was hectic and arduous. The pupils were driven to their limits and more than one dropped out. For their part, the Russian tutors were carefully watching everyone's progress; and at each stage of the course they diligently recorded their comments on every single member of each team. These were filed, day by day, in personal dossiers.

The Soviets had invested a great deal of time and money in these students, and they were determined to get their pound of flesh. In Carlos and Boudia they had clearly made a good choice; both were paying enormous dividends on the investment. However, the difference between the two did not pass unnoticed. For just as the Algerian behaved modestly and with caution, so Carlos, because of his youth and boundless energy, always tended towards flamboyance and recklessness. These facts were recorded.

One evening, Boudia was again listening to Carlos telling his tall stories. This time Carlos was pretending to be a Spaniard, one of an aristocratic family that had fallen on hard times. According to the story, the family emigrated to Venezuela and inter-married with the local Indians, thus making a rare breed. When Carlos had finished talking, Boudia, in a serious vein, said:

'Why do you spread all these tall stories?'

'Perhaps because I subconsciously want to sever all links with my past,' Carlos said. 'You know, I only came of age when I reached twenty and had formed my own view of the world. What came before that doesn't exist for me any more. Maybe I'm trying to widen the rift, to conceal who I truly am and where I sprang from. I'm not at all sure.'

47

There was a pause, unbroken by Boudia, who knew better than to interrupt such a rare confession.

'I'm preparing for my future,' Carlos continued. 'In a way, it's like testing my own ability to lay a smoke-screen. Look at it this way. We all carry false names here. But do you honestly think that I have discovered nothing about the others on the course? I am fully aware of all there is to know about the others, but nobody knows anything about me. They think I'm a playboy. A lover. A story-teller. That's what they think and that's what they admire. And you know why? Because they are idiots! They are children. They are still playing games. Not one of them has tasted reality. They are soft. They are untouched. But you and I, we are different. We are professionals and can understand each other. As for our friends here, we only give them what we think they should know. In this, we are both the same.'

A week later, the Algerian was to record his reactions to Carlos – in a manner that surprised even the Russians.

Each student had been asked to fill out a questionnaire, giving his opinions of the others. Boudia answered with a brief sentence on each – but put down Carlos as the one he would most like to work with. He was the only student to do this. It had not been requested. Then Boudia listed all of Carlos's major qualities, and, in so doing, presented a totally different Carlos from the one described by the rest of the unit.

'He is noteworthy for loyalty and adherence to his objective,' Boudia wrote. 'Even if such an objective were to imply death.'

The snow was piling up. It was a hard winter, even for Moscow, and at Patrice Lumumba University, exhaustion was beginning to set in. To break the harsh pace, a concert was arranged in which each nationality was to present some of its folklore. On the night itself, a blizzard was blowing, but within the hall the atmosphere was warm and festive.

From the moment the curtain rose, coloured spotlights wafted the audience out of their daily routine and into a world of make-believe.

Carlos came on stage at the beginning of the second hour.

A single beam of projected light pin-pointed him in the centre of a silvery halo. Without preamble, he recounted an ancient American Indian legend, a tale of the men who lived off the bounty of the sea, accompanying his words with South American melodies strummed on his guitar. It was a typical Carlos performance, although the audience realized that it was much more polished and sophisticated than usual.

Loud applause confirmed his success, and he bowed in acknowledgement as the spotlight faded. As he slipped behind the scenes, a strong arm encircled his shoulders and a voice demanded angrily:

'Who the hell are you?'

'Carlos,' came the reply, calmly.

'*I* am Carlos!'

The lights on stage now focussed on a pair of Basque dancers, but in the gloom of the wings two men of equal height and astounding similarity stood facing each other. One was Carlos, the genuine Carlos – but he was *not* the man who had just come off stage. The performer, made up to perfection to look exactly like the most popular student at the University, simply stood where he was and a broad smile flowered on his face.

'Don't you recognize me, Carlos?'

This time the voice was different, more guttural. The voice of the Algerian.

Carlos was dumbfounded.

'Pierre . . . You would have fooled my mother!'

'You mean the Doña Elba Sanchez of Caracas, Venezuela . . .?' said Boudia with a laugh. 'I just wanted to show you how you look, how you sing and act.'

Carlos had discovered another facet of his Algerian friend's many-sided personality – the professional make-up man and actor.

Then, as the Basques left the stage, he turned and tugged Boudia with him into the spotlight. The audience was stunned by the unexpected appearance of two Carloses.

'Friends, you must surely be thinking that you saw me

here five minutes ago. Well, you are wrong – you saw him playing me!' Carlos pointed to Boudia.

The hall now rocked with laughter. Carlos the story-teller was in top form! Nobody believed his declaration; it had to be another well-prepared leg-pull for their entertainment. But then the two men began to play and sing a duet, and the laughter died away, to be replaced by perplexed murmurs. Which was the real Carlos? As the song ended, the curtain came down and then rose again, to reveal only one Carlos. The other had vanished, but which man remained it was impossible to tell, so uncanny had been the resemblance between the two performers standing on stage a few seconds before.

Most of the audience forgot the incident, but two men remembered: later in their lives they would play out the game on a far more deadly level.

The terrorist course was nearing its end, but Boudia still had no idea of the price that would be demanded of him in return for the hospitality and training given by the Russians. He was soon to find out.

A few days before the formal ending of the course, Boudia was told to report to the administrative building. Two men were waiting for him in an inner room. They greeted him with smiles and handshakes.

'Sit down, Boudia.'

It was the first time in months he had heard his real name uttered. This alone was enough to tell him that things were now about to change drastically.

Seated at a table on which stood a samovar of tea, Boudia and the two men began a conversation that was to last throughout most of the day. During this time the two Russians painted a complex picture, parts of which had already been obvious to Boudia, parts of which now became clear for the first time.

Marxist ideology, they said, required the offering of tangible aid to left-wing organizations operating underground, wherever in the world they were to be found. The objective – the installation of progressive regimes in all countries – was shared by the Soviet Union and many others; but all assistance was useless unless there were men who fervently believed in the dream of communist progress.

'Let us talk frankly,' one of the men then said. 'We share complete understanding of your desire to overthrow the existing regime in your homeland, and to reinstate the previous leftist order. But the truth is that, after thorough investigation, we have found a slightly different picture from that which you painted. The results of our investigation are far from encouraging. Boumedienne is firmly in power, and there are few signs of any serious underground movement. We do know of the existence of a few left-wing groups, but there is no realistic basis for immediate operations.'

The Algerian knew that his informant's data was basically correct. But was this an indication that the Russians were retreating from the alliance they had promised him? The Russian in front of him had obviously anticipated this question.

'We are not abandoning the idea,' he said. 'But it will have to wait for the future, when the time is ripe. It may be a matter of years before . . .'

'And till then?' Boudia interrupted impatiently.

The Russian smiled. 'I'm glad you asked,' he said. 'There is a lot we can do until then – if we can find a common language – and I personally believe that we can.'

The Russians then spent the next hour describing the web of active terrorist organizations throughout the world. Dealing with each in turn, they noted that these organizations operated without outside backing or assistance.

'If we could establish contact between these groups, respectable achievements could result. We would also be able to encourage the seeds of revolt in your own country.'

Although he guessed that this was merely a sop thrown in to calm his impatience, Boudia said:

'You are speaking as though you were planning to create some sort of international underground.'

'Precisely,' the Russian replied, glancing briefly at his companion. 'Our aim is to reach a common language and

51

arrange for mutual aid between these nationalist organizations. You could be of assistance in this, and, in return, we will help you with your own problem when the time is ripe. More than that: if your plans succeed, you will have at your disposal far greater tools than any the Soviet Union could offer you today.'

'I am interested,' Boudia said.

The Russian smiled. 'I never doubted we would find a common ground,' he said.

The other Russian now described the plan that has since been code-named 'Terror International' by Western security forces, stressing, as he did so, the benefits that would accrue to each organization joining the happy band of comrades. Then, close to noon, this same Russian introduced a new element.

'What do you think of the Palestinian organizations?' he asked.

'I respect them,' Boudia said. 'They are fighting for a cause close to my own heart. But I regret to say they haven't achieved much yet.'

'Indeed,' the Russian said. 'And this is the one field where you could contribute.'

Boudia reflected on the proposition. He felt a debt to the Arab world. During the Algerian revolt, the Arab countries had given solid support to the FLN struggle. In fact, Egypt had often served as a base for their leaders, and other Arab countries had contributed money and arms. Then, again, Boudia shared a common bond of culture and religious heritage with the Arabs.

It seemed to Boudia that, despite all his earlier fears, he *would* be able to pay the Soviet price without selling his soul to the devil. They were asking him to work with the Beirut-established Popular Front for the Liberation of Palestine. Since France was already serving as a base of operations, the Russians suggested that Boudia operate from Paris. Parallel to PFLP operations, he would be expected to propagate the concept of an underground international network as quickly as possible. Money and other aid would be provided. His reward, they agreed, would be immediate encouragement to the progressive left in Algeria. Then, when the time came for more dramatic activity in Algeria, he would receive money, weapons and even manpower, via the new international alliance.

'It is quite likely that, in the course of your work, you will encounter many of your companions from here. You should know that all your group will be working in operational and intelligence roles within the various Palestinian organizations. If you have need to call on them for help, your time here should have helped you select the men you most want.'

Clearly the Russians were playing a magnificent chess game, with every move well considered in advance. Boudia had to admire their ambition and thoroughness.

He parted from the two Russians – who he would never see again – with a warm handshake.

Boudia came down in the pre-dawn darkness to the car that was waiting to take him to the airport. It was snowing heavily and he shivered with cold. One man stood alone in the entrance to the building. Carlos.

'I came to say farewell, amigo.'

They smiled at each other. The snow swirled about them. The wind howled across the tarmac, around the buildings. They both felt as if the scene were unreal.

'How did you know?' Boudia asked. 'It was supposed to be secret.'

Carlos shrugged and grinned. 'Never mind how I knew,' he said. 'I knew. That's all that matters. So I came.'

Carlos embraced him. They felt close at that moment. 'Good luck,' Carlos said, and stepped back, stopping just by the entrance. Boudia smiled. He put his bags in the waiting car. Then, as he opened the door to climb in, he looked back at the figure in the darkness, just standing there, motionless.

'Hello, Carlos!' Boudia said, trying to lighten the sadness of departure by employing the catch-phrase they had often used in moments of jest. 'Hello, Carlos! Farewell!'

Carlos waved his hand. The Algerian felt near to tears. He

turned around, climbed into the car, and was driven to the aircraft that would fly him to Paris and the bloody deeds of an amazing organization.

Terror International.

PART TWO:

TERROR INTERNATIONAL

CHAPTER FIVE

THE MINI-SKIRTS THAT MISFIRED

An unseasonal wave of dry heat blew across central Israel on 11th April, 1971. Towards evening the air cooled, but the temperature inside the buildings of Lod Airport remained oppressively high – perhaps hinting at the hot summer to come that year.

Despite the unexpected change in the weather, it was business as usual, as plane after plane arrived and departed on schedule. None of the personnel at the airport sensed anything extraordinary in the air – but extraordinary was the only word to describe the events which took place during the next few hours.

For in later years the details of the 'mini-skirt affair' would be recognized as the first halting steps of the Terror International campaign, masterminded in Russia, against the whole Western world.

Less than two years had elapsed since Muhamad Boudia and his friend Carlos had been turned loose by the Russians. Their aim, as they had been carefully briefed, was to set in motion the network of terror which the Kremlin hoped would help weaken the whole fabric of Western democracy. In fact, it was the Algerian who was to set the pace from his head-quarters established in the French capital – for Paris had been chosen as the main centre from which the movement would be directed.

If the Arabs were active in their underground cells in France, so were the agents of the Israeli Mossad Habitachon (Defence Institute), known commonly as 'Mossad'. And it was information gleaned from two attractive but indiscreet girls in Paris which prompted five men to drive to Lod Airport, Israel, that fateful evening of 11th April, 1971.

Patiently, the five men sat waiting in a small air-conditioned room in the office block of the Customs Administration. Two of the group were officers in the Israel Police Special Branch, from National HQ in Jerusalem. They were there under direct orders of Deputy Commissioner Aharon Chelouche. The other three, in civilian clothes, belonged to Mossad, then headed by Major-General Zvi Zamir.

The telephone rang. The senior policeman present, a chief superintendant, picked up the receiver. The conversation was brief and to the point. Orders were relayed down the line and, turning to his colleagues, the officer said:

'Gentlemen, the plane has landed.'

To the passengers boarding the bus on the tarmac, there was nothing exceptional about their arrival in the Holy Land. They were involved in the usual scramble for places to sit on the bus; and minutes later the crowd of men and women – looking no different from the average mixture of humanity coming and going at any international airport anywhere in the world – were passing through the glass doors at the passport control hall.

Discreetly, the five men moved to a hidden vantage point near the passport control booths, which were manned by the normal policemen on routine duty. Nothing seemed amiss. A ragged queue formed, with passengers clutching passports.

In fact, each passport was being checked against the lists of 'wanted' persons placed below desk level to hide them from the gaze of the new arrivals. Passports were then stamped and their owners headed towards customs – the usual procedure.

The police sergeant in booth number two looked down at the passport on his desk. It was French. The photograph before him indicated that the owner was a rare beauty, and the officer, lifting his head, found himself looking into the eyes of a very lovely girl. She smiled at him and, nearly forgetting his official bearing, he smiled back. Then, flustered, he put his head down again to study the details of the passport and, almost as an afterthought, to check the 'wanted' list.

Suddenly he froze.

The name he had just read in the passport stared straight back at him from the 'wanted' list, a name heavily underlined in thick black pencil. The sergeant checked again, but there was no doubt about it. The twenty-one-year-old beauty, Martine Ellen Garcier, was delectable; but she was also, most certainly, a ripe candidate for special attention.

Now fully alert, the sergeant gave the senior official nearby a discreet glance. And, as he did so, he deliberately started slowing up his normally efficient passport routine.

This delay, brief as it was, seemed to annoy the waiting girl.

'I'm in a hurry,' she said, a spark of anger in her voice, and her French, as the sergeant mechanically observed, containing a touch of North African inflexion.

'Just a minute, miss,' he replied in English, deliberately hesitating in order to give his superior time to react without attracting attention.

Even as he spoke, another passenger – a girl just as dazzling as his own client, though a few years older, and who had already passed through customs – called out in an annoyed tone: 'Monsieur, please give my friend her passport. It is clearly in order, and we are tired and want to get to our hotel.'

Both girls, he noticed, were dressed in the briefest of miniskirts which served to emphasize their superb, sun-tanned legs.

By now the officer who had been in the background was talking to the older girl.

'May I look at your passport, Mademoiselle?' he said politely. 'Just a routine check . . .'

The girl flushed and handed over her passport. The official studied it carefully. According to the document, the girl's name was Danielle Rivet. Neither this official nor his companions knew under which name the accomplice of Martine Ellen Garcier would be travelling; all that the message from a top Mossad agent had said was: 'Stop and detain female Garcier. Also second female travelling with her. Name not known.' However, the official, basing his suspicions solely on the two girls' nervous impatience, was convinced that he had who they were looking for.

By now Martine Garcier had been marched up to the official by the passport control officer. Turning to both young ladies, the official said politely but firmly:

'Ladies, I must ask you to accompany me. A minor discrepancy. No more.'

The two girls did not go quietly. Again, betraying their lack of professionalism, they let fly at the police with a stream of abuse and outrage, speaking in a very fast, colloquial French; and it was only when three other uniformed men, all clearly armed, had joined the little group that the girls seemed to lose their self-confidence and exchanged quick, fearful glances. They looked down at the floor as the officers took them by the arms and marched them away to a secluded near-by office.

Few passengers noticed the incident.

And now the two girls, their blonde hair cascading over their shoulders and their lovely legs crossed, sat facing experienced and determined interrogators.

Both girls pretended indignation. They claimed that they were just innocent secretaries who had saved hard to buy their air tickets to visit the holy places of Jerusalem. Then, taking refuge in anger and humiliation, they threatened to complain to the French Ambassador about this uncalled for 'impertinence'. The police officers ignored this. They merely posed routine questions. While they did so, their watchful companions sat waiting their turn.

'Name?'

'Danielle Rivet.'

'Age?'

'Twenty-six.'

'Occupation?'

'Secretary.'

'Address?'

'Paris.'

Then the turn of the second girl.

'Name?'

'Martine Ellen Garcier.'

'Age?'

'Twenty-one.'

Time and again, the most simple questions – simple, polite, repetitive and exhausting – questions that particularly infuriated Danielle who, now thinking that the investigation wasn't straying out of the realm of routine harassment, gained enough courage to counter-attack.

'I'll publish your rudeness and insolence in the Paris papers,' she said. 'I demand to know why you are wasting our time by detaining us in this manner.'

'It's not worth getting angry,' the senior official replied. 'We simply want to check a few points, and we expect you to co-operate.'

'So?' Danielle said. 'What, precisely, do you want to know?'

'Why did you come to Israel?'

'I told you. We both came to visit the holy places.'

The official sighed wearily, disbelievingly. And by now the hidden fear that gnawed away at Danielle was beginning to distort her lovely features. She began to shout wildly.

'Is it because I am a Christian that you are bullying me?' she shouted. 'Do you mistreat your Jewish visitors this way?'

The official was unperturbed. By now it was clear to him that the girls were guilty, and that Danielle Rivet was the leader of the two. After all, it had been her intemperate behaviour which had given them both away at passport control. Deciding to ignore her completely, he turned to the other girl.

'Mademoiselle,' he said. 'Don't you agree that there is a striking resemblance between yourself and Danielle Rivet?'

'So what?' Martine flashed back, obviously encouraged by the aggression of her older companion. 'You look just like all the other officers!'

'True,' her interrogator replied evenly. 'We are roughly the same age. We wear the same uniforms . . .'

'Well, then, it's the same with us,' Martine said. 'Our hair, our skirts, our age ... But come to Paris and you won't be able to tell the difference between hundreds of young girls.'

'What's your name?'

Automatically, the girl started to blurt out the real answer, but then she checked herself, hesitated and blushed.

'Garcier,' she said. 'Martine Ellen Garcier. I've told you so many times. And it's there in my passport.'

The official smiled. 'Yes,' he said slowly. 'Same hair, same skirts, same age ...' Then he leaned forward, looked Martine right in the eye, and said deliberately: 'Same lies, too, I would say.'

The girls flushed in anger, but the officer stood up and walked away without even waiting for an answer.

The group of men in the room now ignored the two North African girls, behaving as though they had completely lost interest in them. Total silence reigned in the room. This was a deliberate ploy to make the two girls feel confused, alone and defenceless. The break in interrogation also served the purpose of giving customs men time to find the girls' luggage and bring it into the room next door.

Eventually the telephone rang on the desk in front of the couple, and the officer in charge, after a brief word in Hebrew into the phone, left the room.

Martine and Danielle, now sitting alone in the room, looked nervously at each other, but said nothing. They were left a long time. This, also, was deliberate. Then, when the officials came back into the room, Martine Garcier covered her face with her hands and Danielle bit her lower lip.

The suitcases, unopened, were placed on the carpet, and both girls knew that the contents would damn them.

'Open the suitcases,' the senior officer said.

Danielle looked up at him. She was angry and frightened. She put her hand in one pocket and pulled out her keys and threw them quite violently at the officer.

'*You* open them!' she snapped.

The officer opened her suitcases. He studied them a long time. Then he looked at Danielle and smiled slightly.

'Yours?' he said formally.

'Yes,' Danielle whispered, her voice starting to break. 'But

61

the contents ... I didn't know ...' She stared up at the officer and a hint of anger came back to her eyes. 'I know nothing about it,' she said. 'Perhaps you arranged it yourself.'

'Enough,' the officer said, now speaking very firmly. 'You are Nadia Bardeli, from Morocco. And you,' he added, turning to the other girl, 'are Nadia's sister Marlene. You are both under arrest.'

The investigation was now turned over to the Mossad men, who began coldly and methodically to tear apart the remaining shreds of the girls' resistance.

Both knew that they had been betrayed even before their arrival at Lod Airport.

Inspection of the suitcases had brought to light a lethal quantity of explosives. Then policewomen took the sisters to another room, where a search of their clothing revealed that hidden in their well-padded brassières, as well as in specially-made belts strapped to their lovely bodies, was further sabotage material.

The girls cracked completely.

Their confessions came spilling out in such a disjointed, incoherent babble of self-incrimination that the Mossad men had to re-play the tape-recordings made of the interrogations time and again before they could piece together the whole story in a logical sequence. It was a complex, fascinating and highly revealing story – and its central character was the man known as Muhamad Boudia ...

Coming under the sway of the 'New Left' teachings of their university friends in Paris, Marlene and Nadia Bardeli were invited to numerous parties in the French capital, where they were introduced to men who were 'taking active steps' to bring down 'the corrupt, bourgeois-ridden society' around them.

At one of these gatherings in the Rue des Ecoles in the Latin Quarter, they met the fascinating Muhamad Boudia. By now, this former terrorist was a highly respected theatre producer and actor who was as generous to the girls with his money as he was with promises to help their careers. It amused the Algerian to capture the hearts of the two sisters, particularly as both were so beautiful. Indeed, there was one delicious moment when they went together to his apartment to taste the more esoteric aspects of his sexual knowledge.

However, as far as Boudia was concerned, this was not just a pleasurable pastime. He had long since set out on a deliberate policy of recruiting young women to act as his agents, or to use their apartments as an oasis of refuge in times of need – the same trick his good friend Carlos was, at that very moment, employing in London.

Daughters of a wealthy Moroccan family, Nadia and Marlene ignored the anomaly of being supported financially by their own solid and loving 'bourgeois' father, slipping quickly, as they were, into the trendy jargon of the 'New Left'.

There was even more excitement in store for the sisters when they were introduced to a pair of Boudia's disciplined and handsome lieutenants, and so persistent in their amorous pursuits were these two new companions that the sisters fell passionately in love with them.

Nadia had formerly worked in Casablanca as a reporter covering literature and the arts for a daily paper – but now, in Paris, she had to make do with a simple secretarial job. Boudia, knowing this, promised to help her find a post on a weekly magazine where the editor, 'an old friend', owed him a favour.

As for Marlene, there was the promise of a glamorous career as an actress dangling before her naïve eyes ...

In the meantime, Boudia wondered if the two girls might do him a small favour. Of course he would pay for their air tickets and all their expenses, as well as giving them plenty of pocket money. What he wanted, he told them, was someone who would transport 'vital' goods to Israel. And he hinted broadly that the sisters would, at the same time, be helping the cause of freedom.

Thrilled by this new adventure, the two girls eagerly accepted the false passports; and several times they rehearsed the roles they were to play after flying in to Lod Airport.

After reaching their hotel in Tel Aviv, the sisters were to collect a 'radio' from two other friends.

Although neither girl knew it, their naïvety was being ruthlessly exploited by Boudia in his attempt to get 'Terror International' off the ground with a spectacular series of bombings in Israel itself.

On the morning following their arrival, the sisters were to phone Pierre and Edith Bourghalter and arrange to meet them at the California Cafe on Frishman Street, near Tel Aviv's busy Dizengoff Street. One of the girls had to carry a copy of *Le Monde* in her right hand; then, once she had been spotted by her contact, he would hand her the radio and the other sabotage material.

As the Israelis were to discover, this innocent 'radio', looking like any other ordinary transistor, was packed full with timing devices and detonators.

To the consternation of Mossad operators, Nadia explained when captured that there was also a fifth member of the team, a 26-year-old girl, whom they had also met in Paris, who was to supervise the whole operation.

After this disclosure, on 12th April, the police detained a certain Francine Adeleine Maria, who in fact turned out to be a terrorist high up on the 'wanted' list. Her real name was Evelyn Baradj, and she had already been involved in one hijacking and numerous sabotage attacks, and was known to move in terrorist circles all over Europe.

Francine, or Evelyn Baradj, was a dedicated Marxist who possessed particularly strong links with the Baader-Meinhof terrorist movement in Germany. Among her other jobs, she had once worked as a teacher in a school in one of the 'red' suburbs of Paris.

Despite her initial protestations of innocence, Evelyn finally admitted that her role in the 'mini-skirt affair' was to prepare the explosives brought to her by the Bardeli sisters. Then, after selecting her targets – major hotels packed with tourists in Jerusalem, Haifa and Tel Aviv – she was to instruct Nadia and Martine where to leave their lethal bombs, all of which would be packed in suitcases. Surely nobody, it was reasoned, would possibly suspect the two charming sisters in their mini-skirts.

Prior to their fateful journey, Boudia left the sisters alone with his willing lieutenants in his apartment. The girls' acute romantic appetites – so expertly manipulated by the Algerian and his men – were now whetted by the prospect of a real-life adventure involving false documents, a plane journey ... and detonators strapped to their stomachs. It was therefore with some eagerness that they now stepped out of their clothes and let their handsome male companions show them just how to wear the 'lucky' belts – as the men jokingly called the elastic holders of lethal equipment.

Meanwhile, Boudia had slipped away to attend to other business.

Unknown to anybody else in the operation, Boudia was also sending along his most trusted agent – not to take part in the actual sabotage work, but merely to act as an observer and learn any necessary lessons which might be useful for future reference.

The Algerian smiled gently as he met this accomplice in a café within sight of the Notre Dame Cathedral. She returned his smile as he leaned over the table and said:

'Not wearing your Calèche perfume today?'

For indeed, this was none other than the girl who had so fascinated him, nearly two years back, when he had first met her at Patrice Lumumba University. The girl who had mistaken him for Carlos.

The Russians had efficiently arranged matters so that each group they trained separately in Moscow would in future operate as a single team. Mademoiselle Calèche, as Boudia still called her, had never forgotten her love for Carlos; but she had also become the mistress of Boudia, a relationship started when Carlos had first ordered her to the Algerian's empty bed. Now, she appreciated the Algerian's mature strength, just as much as she was held by the fiery, impetuous passion of the younger man.

Operating under the name of Nicole, the tall, elegantly

65

dressed young woman looked and behaved quite differently from most of the other females found in the ranks of the terrorist movements in Europe. While they wore jeans and scorned the bourgeois trappings of 'decadent' cosmetics and jewellery, Nicole was always expensively, and beautifully, dressed.

Today was no exception.

Looking at her, Boudia wondered who she really was, wondered where she got her money from; particularly since, alone among the operators, she never asked for funds or expenses.

How could she afford such clothes? And how could she afford that luxurious apartment on the Avenue Foch, alongside the homes of such famous millionaires as Aristotle Onassis and Prince Rainier of Monaco? She never spoke of such matters.

Nevertheless, Nicole's excellent education, her intelligence and, above all, her costly wardrobe all served as the perfect cover for her work as a courier. No passport official was likely to suspect that this rich and elegant woman was working for the destruction of the established order.

Now Nicole was worried about the Lod Airport operation.

Right from the beginning, Nicole had expressed her opposition to the use of 'amateurs' for such important missions. She also felt that the Algerian's normally sharp judgement had been dulled by the obvious charms of the two Bardeli sisters.

She now repeated these doubts to Boudia, but he waved them aside. It was his belief that in certain circumstances amateurs were better at escaping undetected. Nicole wasn't convinced, but she bowed to Boudia's wishes, insisting only that under no circumstances were either the sisters, or even the Baradj girl, to be told that their operation was being observed by her. Boudia agreed.

Thus it was that, a few days later, when the Mossad men closed in on the Commodore Hotel in Tel Aviv to arrest the 69-year-old Pierre Bourghalter and his 60-year-old wife – the pair who had passed on the sabotage material to the previously captured Bardeli sisters – the Israelis were quite

66

unaware of the fact that an even bigger fish had been within their grasp . . .

Nicole was, in fact, seated in a restaurant nearby even as the protesting Bourghalters were being escorted into police cars before being driven off to headquarters in Motzkin Boulevard. Outwardly calm, but seething inwardly with anger, she observed the collapse of the whole operation.

Minutes later she was in a bus heading for Jerusalem.

As she sat in the bus, slowly and laboriously grinding its way up the steep hills to Jerusalem from the plain below where Tel Aviv is situated, her sharp wits brought her to the conclusion that either the Bourghalters or the Bardeli sisters had spoken too freely in Europe, and that some alert Mossad spy had got wind of the plan in time to warn the Israelis.

It could not have been the Bourghalters, she decided, knowing that they had been in it purely and simply for the money, and that their greed would have kept their lips tight. No, she was convinced that, just as she had feared, those 'amateurs', the mini-skirted Bardeli sisters, had broken down and talked.

Her anger – tinged with a faint hint of jealousy at the thought of Boudia succumbing to the girls – quickly subsided; and her mind, now cool, thought more clearly.

If the Israeli counter-intelligence men knew about the Bardeli girls, she reasoned, they might also have linked them with Boudia. Even worse, the Mossad might have been smart enough to put two and two together, thereby stumbling on that ambitious plan that included setting up an international network where the terrorists would pool their resources to strike not only at Israel, but at the West as well.

She *had* to know who had broken their Paris defences.

Strolling through the ancient city's Jaffa Gate, Nicole stopped to buy a glass of fresh orange juice from an Arab stallholder. A few minutes later she disappeared among the crowds of sightseers in the Street of David, then slipped into a shop filled with hundreds of coarsely-carved olivewood statuettes and other tourist trinkets.

'Can I help you, Mademoiselle?' the assistant asked in

67

French, guessing her origins through long experience of handling the hordes of visitors to the Holy Land.

'Haven't you anything of better quality?' Nicole said with a show of distaste, handling the crudely made figure of yet another Virgin Mary. Then, beneath her breath so that only he could hear, she said a few words in Arabic – which words made the young man turn pale with fright.

Nicole was taking a major risk in coming to see her contact right here in Old Jerusalem, under the very noses of the Israeli army patrols that sauntered up and down the winding streets. It was a grave risk, but it was one she had to take as she was desperately worried.

Clearly, the Israeli secret police had got wind of the bomb plot – and she suspected that all five of the team were now in the hands of the Mossad, probably telling them all they wanted to know. It was therefore absolutely essential that she make contact with the agent who had been planted, with great difficulty, in Old Jerusalem. She had to glean any information she could about how the project had been uncovered in Paris even before it got under way.

Thus she risked everything by making contact with the frightened assistant whom she knew could lead her to the man she now wanted.

Within minutes, the pale and trembling young Arab had taken her to a tiny Oriental café not far from the St. Anna's Church at the Gate of St. Stephen's, deep in the Moslem quarter of the old city.

Nicole's instincts had been correct.

From the information she now received, the death warrant of one of Israel's top agents was signed and sealed.

It would be some time before Boudia was avenged for the defeat of the mini-skirt operation – but later the Jewish agent would die from a bullet fired by the Algerian in person ...

The arrest of the Bardeli sisters, the Bourghalters and Evelyn Baradj was a moment of triumph for the Mossad.

General Zahir reported to Prime Minister Golda Meir, Defence Minister Moshe Dayan and other key security figures, among them Chief of Staff Haim Bar Lev, Intelligence Chief Aharon Yariv and Police Inspector-General Pinhas Kopel, the full details of the case. There was even time for a joke: 'The PFLP are trying to conquer Israel from the mattresses of their mistresses.' And as one General wryly put it: 'They seem to be better at making love than war.'

However, as security men probed deeper and deeper into the confessions of their handful of captives, the smiles of self-congratulation soon disappeared from their faces.

Within weeks, a long, highly confidential document was being sent to security chiefs and police heads of all Western governments. The message from the highly regarded Israeli secret service organization had to be taken seriously; but none the less, the contents of the report caused deep frowns of reservation on the faces of government officials and Cabinet Ministers involved with security matters.

Unfortunately, many preferred to let matters 'take their natural course' – as one statesman, renowned for his caution and ability to let principles bow before political expediency, was heard to mutter – and this indecisiveness was to cause the loss of dozens of innocent lives all over the Western world before governments had to admit that the Mossad had been right.

An international terrorist movement, skilfully manipulated by the KGB in Moscow, was striking hard not only at tiny, expendable Israel, but at the whole fabric of the democratic way of life.

CHAPTER SIX

A SCEPTICAL AMERICAN

CLIFFORD YOUNG looked out of the window of the plane at the blue Mediterranean and the white houses of Tel Aviv. It was an agreeable sight, particularly so for a man making his first visit to Israel.

The El Al 707 was on a direct flight from New York to Lod. Its passengers were mostly tourists following the spring sun, but this particular American was no holiday-maker. One week after the arrest of Nadia and Marlene Bardeli, his CIA superiors had decided that the time had come for a high level exchange of opinions with the Mossad.

Indeed, the document of the Israeli discovery of a Russian-inspired terrorist network was certainly being taken seriously in Washington – even if European governments still preferred to sweep the matter under the carpet.

For months, CIA experts had been trying to clarify what was going on behind the scenes in the power struggle between East and West. For almost a year now, items of information flowing into the CIA centre at Langley, outside Washington, had been building up into a picture of a change of direction in KGB operations. Yet to know exactly what the Soviet Intelligence arm was up to, the CIA needed more data and the opinions of other experts.

Young's mission was to collect and define whatever information the Israelis were prepared to give him.

The 45-year-old CIA evaluator buckled his seat belt and, watching the parched hills unfolding below, reflected on the reasons for his being hurried to the Holy Land.

A few of his colleagues suspected that the Soviets had

found a new way of trying to undermine the foundations of the West. The Israelis, also, seemed to suspect this.

But if the Israelis had been the first to grasp this fact, then perhaps they had been more than lucky. For it was the unwitting revelations of two very frightened Moroccan girls – their mini-skirts of little use to them as they sat in an Israeli prison – that had caused the alarm bells to ring out loud and clear.

The aircraft had landed. The passengers disembarked. As they began to move into the terminal building, two men got out of a car parked nearby on the tarmac and walked towards the steps. They waited for Young.

He already knew one of them. They had met a few times at information exchange sessions at Langley, and their relationship had not been a warm one. Young had frequently caused intense irritation to the Mossad by his persistent questioning of their information – giving the impression that he always doubted what they said – and so indignant had this particular Israeli been after one session that he tended to think of Young as being 'a WASP, anti-Semitic son-of-a-bitch'. The criticism was unfair: Young's job was to evaluate all information received; thus he treated it all as if it were false until he had proved it otherwise. Unfortunately, when Young was sceptical, he found it difficult to hide his feelings. He was tough and precise; and he saw no reason to be tactful for the sake of politeness.

Little wonder that the Israelis, sometimes over-aggressive about the righteousness of their cause, and understandably proud of their secret service, regarded this particular CIA agent with luke-warm enthusiasm. However, it was for this very reason that Young's chiefs in Washington had sent him to brave the Mossad in their own den: they knew full well that he would not be easily fooled by the Israelis, who might offer distorted information for their own propaganda purposes.

Sitting back in the car, being driven away from the airport by the Israeli agents, Young took in the colourful sights of Jerusalem. A strange and unique aura of sanctity penetrated the tough, no-nonsense American. The forests, hills and intense blue sky blended into a Biblical image of such haunting beauty that, despite himself, he felt his emotions being stirred.

Later, as he stood on the balcony of his hotel room overlooking the city, he allowed himself a few more moments to savour the enchanting atmosphere of Jerusalem. He then turned abruptly on his heels and took a seat at the table.

Five men had just entered and sat down. There were two Sovietologists, two Orientalists, and an expert on international relations. Five young men – three of them PhD graduates, one of them a professor, and the fifth a man without academic qualifications, but with an unbeatable knowledge of his own subject.

Yankele, one of the experts on Kremlin thinking, opened with the Israeli point-of-view.

'In our opinion, the behind-the-scenes activity has to be viewed in the light of sociological changes in the West in the last few years . . .'

In the late 1960's the United States experienced the impact of two waves of mass social violence – one caused by tensions between white and coloured, the other by the extremism of liberal students calling themselves the 'New Left'. The first wave was of clearly racial-orientated riots. In some cities, whole neighbourhoods were razed to the ground by arson and the use of explosives; and snipers claimed many more lives. Then, on the groundswell of these disruptive riots, campuses across the United States started experiencing the seeds of student unrest, ostensibly aimed at forcing the US out of the Vietnam war.

'Following this trend,' the Israeli emphasized, 'it became possible to understand the New Left-sponsored disturbances among students in France and Germany. The KGB made a very thorough study of the phenomenon, and it was this that gave birth to their new line – aimed at weakening the West with a minimum of financial investment and at absolutely no risk to the lives of their own agents.'

'Where exactly are you heading?' Young asked.

'To the concept of anarchy,' the Israeli said. 'The Soviet government began to think in terms of shaking foundations

by the use of local forces, aided and encouraged by
The object would be to show up the weaknesses o
cratic countries, thereby shaking their self-confiden
turmoil would provide fertile ground for the introduc
new clandestine agents.'

'And how do they manage that?' Young persisted.

The man called Yair intervened. 'I believe this map
help,' he said, drawing the curtain away from a large-s
projection of the world, criss-crossed by red and yellow lir
the red flowing from Moscow, the yellow from Peking. 'V
believe that the Russian experts did precisely what we ar
doing now. They simply spread out a map to see what wa:
happening in places where they were not directly involved.
And this is the picture they saw.

'In South America, the Tupamaros and their imitators are
striking at Western-facing governments. Their aim is
simple: to drive these countries into the Marxist camp like
Cuba.

'In Ireland, the IRA ruthlessly steps up its armed struggle
to break loose from Britain, but their real aims are more
sinister than this. Ulster has already become a major
battlefield. Bombs now explode in London.

'In Spain the Basque underground is showing its claws.
They are waging a bitter fight against the Spanish government to gain what they claim is independence for their ancient nation – and to chew off a sizeable part of their
sovereign homeland – which of course will be dominated by
Marxists.

'In Japan the Red Army are on the rampage. In the name
of leftist progress they perpetuate senseless and brutal
crimes.

'In Turkey there are the first nucleii of an underground
known as the Turkish Liberation Army. They, also, have
their roots in the universities, and their aim is to topple the
regime and tilt the country towards the communist world.
Not long ago they murdered the Israeli Consul in Istanbul.

'As for West Germany, there have been indications that
the Baader-Meinhof murder-gang are again gaining in
strength.

'In the Middle East the growing activity of Arab terror groups speaks for itself.'

'And your conclusions?' Young asked.

'The same we would reach if we had an interest in weakening the West and fostering anarchy – unite all these factions under one umbrella – an umbrella known as Terror International.'

The American was still not convinced.

'It's a fascinating theory,' he said. 'But apart from your analysis of what you would do if you were a KGB officer, where, precisely, is your proof? I mean facts, figures, dates – and names.'

There was no hesitation. The Israelis had anticipated this demand. They produced item after item of information, all of it supported by documents, dossiers of exact details, and factual evidence.

Young examined them all in turn, sometimes asking for explanation or clarification. He was brilliant at getting to the heart of each subject and then asking the most awkward questions. His hosts, however, were equal to the challenge, and the CIA man realized that some very solid work had gone into substantiating their theory.

Yet one point still eluded him.

'How do they go about organizing such an operation?'

Again, there was no hesitation.

'Marxist agents have been active in the field, recruiting key men in the terror organizations. They have been trained in Moscow. We have proof of this. They have offered money and arms in return for co-ordinated activity. As for further proof – well, you will soon see it for yourself in the planned activities of terror across various frontiers, with Germans helping Algerians, Arabs being aided by Japanese, and so forth . . .'

Then, without going into precise details of these surmises – for the Israelis were still extracting more background information from the Bardeli sisters and Evelyn Baradj – they spelt out the training programme currently being given at the Patrice Lumumba University in Moscow.

The session ended at seven that evening.

Clifford Young still had four hours before his plane was due to leave for London, where he would change to a Trans-World flight. He wanted to spend the remaining time strolling through the tantalizing alleyways of the Old City.

He did not express his opinions to the Israelis. To their consternation, he simply said that the information they had given him would be relayed to his superiors, leaving them with the impression that their earnest presentation had been made to a closed and prejudiced mind.

Be that as it may, they were determined to show every courtesy to their guest, and after taking him for a meal in the Hassan Afendi Restaurant outside Herod's Gate, they went for a stroll through the winding streets of the Old City, pointing out the sites holy to Jew, Christian and Moslem. Indeed, for a short time, Young was a fascinated tourist, just like any other.

He departed from Jerusalem at 10.30 p.m

Young was tired. Only now, as the plane winged its way to the starry sky above, did the strain of the last day become apparent. He sank back and tried to sleep ... he tried, but he couldn't.

His thoughts repeatedly returned to the concept of Terror International which had so studiously been described by the Israelis. It all seemed too incredible, too huge, too ambitious, to be even remotely connected to any political reality.

He tilted his seat back, lit a cigarette and began to review the facts he had been given. He added them up; he shuffled them around. He tried to see through his own prejudices – and those of the Israelis – and come up with the cold, irrefutable truth. Then suddenly he sat upright.

The Israelis were correct. The jigsaw pieces made a whole. Now spinning incessantly, tormentingly in his brain, was one stunning, shattering thought:

'Terror International exists!'

CHAPTER SEVEN

SWORDS ARE UNSHEATHED

MUHAMAD BOUDIA was dejected. And for once he did not even try to hide his true feelings, now mirrored so plainly in his cloudy eyes and drooping shoulders. In a quiet corner of a reception lounge at Orly Airport, Nicole looked at him coldly. She had telephoned immediately on arrival in Paris, after a complicated journey which had taken her from Tel Aviv to London, to Beirut, then back again, via London, to the French capital.

Nicole had not even responded with her usual intimate and secret smile at Boudia's teasing 'Mademoiselle Calèche' greeting. Instead, she seemed anxious to get the conversation over with as soon as possible; and certainly she was not prepared to return to his apartment with him as he had hoped.

It was clear to Boudia that the disaster in Tel Aviv, when his five-man team had ended up in an Israeli prison, was being held very much against him – and he knew that the blame was indeed entirely his own.

For a start, he had suffered a heavy loss of face in the terrorist movement. And now the cold anger flashing from Nicole's eyes reflected her earlier opposition to his use of the 'bungling amateurs', as the French girl had scathingly described the Moroccan sisters.

However, Nicole had not taken the unusual step of summoning Boudia to the airport merely to express recriminations. She had in fact brought a message from Dr. George Habash, the fanatical leader of the extremist PFLP terrorist organization, and of both Boudia and Carlos.

'He raved on like a madman,' Nicole said. 'He has taken it

as a personal blow to his pride. He feels that all the other Arab groups are laughing at him – and you know how touchy he can be.'

Boudia smiled wearily at her. The news, after all, was not entirely unexpected and he had resigned himself to this abuse.

'Habash,' Nicole continued, 'is replacing Fuad Elsmali, our contact man, with Michel Mukarbal, who is coming to see you here in Paris within the next day or two.'

Again, these tidings hardly seemed a major cause for concern. What difference did it make which monkey brought its master's message? In any event, none of this could have been the cause of the intense irritation being displayed by the normally unruffled Nicole.

Apart from this one failure, Boudia knew that he had been highly successful in setting up the 'Freedom Fighters International' roof organization, as he had termed it. There had been an encouraging response from the heads of other terror movements throughout Europe – so much so that Boudia knew that his own status in the PFLP, backed by the Russians, was more than secure.

In particular, he had received significant encouragement from the Japanese Red Army, who had sent Furoya Yutaka, their Operations Officer, all the way to Paris to discuss a plan for 'future co-operation'. This meeting had sent Boudia's spirits soaring, for Yutaka had relayed the news that Fusaka Shiganovu, the commander of the Japanese group, was wholly in agreement with the idea of working together. Indeed, Shiganovu had been quick to appreciate how the effectiveness of each terrorist group working in isolation could be increased a hundredfold by presenting a united front.

But Boudia's success went even further than this.

Threats from the terror movements against the oil-rich Arab leaders had encouraged them to open their purses – and they had handed over millions of dollars without the slightest complaint. Anything for peace and quiet – that appeared to be their attitude – and besides, the multi-millionaire Sheiks knew that all they had to do was squeeze the oil companies of the nervous Western governments a little more and their coffers would be replenished in no time. Indeed, this tactic was used with devastating success after the Yom Kippur War, sending the price of oil so high that the economies of the democracies were sorely shaken.

Thus, with unlimited funds at his disposal, Boudia had shrewdly held out a financial bait to members of such organizations as the Baader-Meinhof in Germany and even the Japanese Red Army – and it was for this reason that the path to co-operation had proved much easier than the KGB had anticipated. Also, as an added bonus, the Russians no longer had to spend a single rouble to finance the operation – it was all being financed by the Western countries through their inflated oil payments!

Knowing how successful he had been, the Algerian was confident that the anger George Habash had passed on to Nicole would soon melt away. And after all, the terrorist leader, sitting in safety in Beirut, needed Boudia as much as Boudia needed him.

Then came the sting in the French girl's message.

Her voice softened into concern as she explained to Boudia that the damage done to him by the Moroccan girls was worse than he could possibly have guessed. Thanks to their indiscretion, the Mossad had obtained a lead into the identities of Boudia's Paris unit.

From information gathered in Old Jerusalem, Nicole doubted that the Israelis knew it was Boudia himself who was the head of the international terrorist movement; but she made her warning quite clear:

'Their operatives are moving into Europe. Their attitude has now changed, and they are coming out of Israel to wage war on a worldwide scale against anyone they think opposes them. That includes us, Boudia.'

Now Boudia realized why she had been so angry. He had placed himself in grave danger, quite unnecessarily, through the miserable error of letting the Bardeli sisters do his dirty work for him. The easy times were over; from now on he would have to watch his every step. He would have to kill the men who were after him . . . or be killed by them.

CHAPTER EIGHT

ENTER BARUCH COHEN

THE damage done to the terrorist cause by Nadia and Marlene Bardeli was in fact far greater than either Boudia or Nicole suspected. And the breach in security had occurred right there in Paris even before the girls had set off on their mission.

The Algerian had made the mistake of sending the girls out to various social gatherings in the company of two of his favourite lieutenants, including his most trusted right-hand man, Mahmud Hamshari. Then, at one of these parties, the girls had met a young Arab nationalist – one of the most fervent anti-Israeli Arabs to be found in this New Left social circle. A man known as Yishai.

Indeed, there were times when even those who shared his feelings thought Yishai was a bit of a bore, raving on, as he did in his rich and flowing Arab tongue, about the misdeeds of the Jews in Palestine.

However, this young man was particularly attentive towards Nadia Bardeli, frequently listening instead of talking, and the naïve young girl, flattered by his attention, could not resist boasting that she, too, was 'playing a part' in the struggle against contemptible Israel.

'Oh?' Yishai said, raising his eyebrows and looking sceptical. 'How can a young lady like you, who spends her time in a social whirl, know anything about the politics of the East?'

Nettled by this challenge, Nadia divulged some of the secrets of her forthcoming mission. Needless to say, her companion was impressed. He invited her to dinner the next night at the Tour d'Argent, one of Paris' most distinguished restaurants.

The girl was fed well. She was given a lot to drink. She was flattered and teased and seduced – and she talked quite a lot. In fact, not only did she talk, she also showed Yishai her passport, a false passport, a passport for sabotage, the key to the whole plot.

Thus it was that, through the charms of one man and the naïvety of one girl, the Mossad were given a wealth of advance details about the ill-fated mini-skirt project.

For Moshe Hanan Yishai was not what he appeared.

Yishai was actually called Baruch Cohen. Born in Haifa, he had spent his early life mixing freely with Arab children; thus he knew their language as well as he knew his own. However, Cohen's affinity with the Arab world was based on something other than mere language. Baruch and his five brothers were so close to their Arab friends that they understood thoroughly their customs and way of thinking, and in time even came to look like them.

There was, however, a difference in outlook and upbringing.

Baruch's great grand-father had been Chief Rabbi of Haifa towards the end of the Ottoman Empire period in the history of Palestine – when the dead hand of Turkish rule still hung heavy over the land. The family had emigrated to the country five generations previously; and in their home in Hashomer Street, in the harbour city, Baruch and his brothers were educated in Biblical Judaism and modern Zionist lore.

Baruch was only thirteen when one of his brothers, Yehuda, was killed on the approaches to Rafiah while fighting against invading Arab armies, shortly after Israel declared its independence in 1948. The event made a deep impression on Baruch, for he had been exceptionally close to Yehuda and was later to name his first born after him.

In many ways, Baruch's upbringing was similar to that of a great many Haifa youngsters. After passing through the French-orientated Alliance Primary School, he studied for three years in Haifa's elite Reali Secondary School. In his final year there, the boy decided to join a group of Israeli Scouts in Kibbutz Tel-Reem in the Negev desert. Then, enlisting in the army in 1952, Baruch chose to serve in a combat intelligence unit.

Right from the beginning Baruch stood out as a particularly talented intelligence officer. He had a special gift for learning different languages; and he was cool and intelligent and courageous. His superiors were pleased with him.

When Baruch married Nurit, the girl he had met in a kibbutz and fallen in love with, she was well aware of the dangerous nature of his job which took him away from home so often. The couple had a second son, Haim, as well as Yehuda, but naturally enough the two youngsters knew nothing of the specialized espionage experience their father gained while on numerous active missions.

It was only in the days after the Six Day War that the talents of Baruch Cohen truly bore fruit.

The terrorist organizations had begun to recruit sabotage teams on the West Bank of Jordan, now Israeli-occupied territory. To counter this menace, the Israelis sent in agents who mixed freely with the Arabs; and so successful were Baruch and his fellow counter-intelligence men that terrorist groups were rounded up as fast as they were formed. Indeed for years after, Baruch would be held up as the man largely responsible for crushing the Arab attempt to ferment revolt in the occupied territories.

But now an even more important mission awaited this young Haifa-born intelligence officer. The Israelis decided to move out from Israel itself and strike at the terror groups wherever they were to be found – and Baruch Cohen's name immediately sprang into the minds of the alert Mossad chiefs.

So, with his wife and young children, Cohen – now working under the cover name of Moshe Hanan Yishai – boarded a plane from Lod to Brussels. The date was 15th July, 1970.

In Brussels, Baruch was given a minor post in the Israeli Embassy, a job which enabled him to rove all over Europe without arousing the slightest suspicion, either in diplomatic circles or among Western Security establishments. Fluent in Arabic as well as European languages, he had no trouble in finding his way about; but eventually he chose to go more and more to Paris where, at numerous New Left parties, he was now accepted without question as a man with a burning hatred for 'Israeli Imperialists'. In fact, this task was made all the easier for him by the natural tendency of the Arabs to magnify their deeds and to boast about forthcoming events. As Baruch himself said: 'Anybody can come away from these meetings, once he is accepted as a friend, with profitable material.'

Gradually, Baruch got to know every corner and alleyway of the Latin Quarter in Paris; and he was introduced more frequently to the big names in the Arab terrorist movements, all of whom regarded Paris, in the early 1970's, as a safe haven from which to operate – thanks to the pro-Arab policies of President Charles de Gaulle. And, in the end, Baruch even got to know the actual hide-outs of the different terrorist members.

Naturally, there was enormous jubilation in Jerusalem as Baruch Cohen, alias Yishai, sent a growing volume of information out of Paris – and the advance information about the sabotage team which included the Bardeli sisters, electrified Mossad headquarters in Israel.

Baruch Cohen was also excited. Not only had he enabled the Mossad to arrest the whole group before they could carry out their operation, but he had also discovered that the suave Arabs who had introduced the girls to the New Left parties were 'big shots' in the 'terror international' organization.

Meanwhile, in Mossad headquarters, there was now a recognition that the 'mini-skirt' affair had been a vital turning point in the current terror war. This fresh challenge had to be met by hastening the process of uncovering the ringleaders of the PFLP in Europe and the emerging, but as yet shadowy 'Terror International' movement. More: the war against the terrorists was to be stepped up by sending out

Israeli executioners to wherever these men were to be found. And once found, they were to be killed.

This, in turn, meant bringing fresh operatives into the field and sending out new orders to those already working all over Europe.

An assessment of the task in hand was brought to Baruch Cohen by a special Mossad representative just three weeks after the Bardeli sisters had been captured in Tel Aviv. The meeting took place in a back room of the Israeli Embassy in the Belgian city, and the two men, who were old friends, settled down to a long and detailed talk over innumerable cups of coffee.

'The terrorists have changed tactics,' Baruch was told. 'They were completely defeated – as you know only too well – in trying to stir up sabotage in Israel itself and among the Arabs of the West Bank. They are now in a position where they no longer dare send their men across our frontiers; so they are recruiting romantic innocents, as well as fools, and men and women who will do anything for money. They are being offered unlimited amounts of oil dollars.

'However, if this were the only problem it would not be so serious. What *is* serious is that terror is now to be used as a weapon against the whole of the Western World. The communists have helped this process along, taking advantage of the anarchist and terrorist organizations already existing in Europe, Latin America and Japan. The Marxists and Maoists are being trained in Moscow, and the terror groups in the Arab world are going along with this – for their aim is no longer simply to strike at Jews and Israelis: they are sowing terror in the West in an effort to isolate the State of Israel.

'As you know, they kill and maim hundreds of innocent men, women and children by planting their bombs in aircraft, in shops, in restaurants, in the streets of Athens, London, Paris and elsewhere. They slaughter indiscriminately, murdering and maiming citizens who have nothing whatsoever to do with Israel. Naturally, this does not do us any good.

'The Western leaders are, for the most part, acting just as the Arab terrorists want them to. They put the blame on us, saying that the Arab "patriots" are merely frustrated by our "obstinacy" in not giving in to their demands. Thus, because of the pressure being put on Israel, we are becoming more and more isolated. The Western governments do not seem to realize that the terror they refuse to meet firmly will, in the end, destroy Western democracy itself.

'The international terror campaign is, then, designed to isolate us from the West, and because the instigators are now reaping the fruits of their labour, they are about to step up the action. They are also trying to persuade more foreigners to come to Israel and do their dirty work for them.

'It was thanks to you that we managed to stop those two girls before they completed their mission – but we have to get to the heart of this rotten business. We know they are planning further strikes at us in Israel, so if the Western authorities won't attempt to wipe them out, we will have to do it ourselves. We must now move out of the role of simply gathering information. We have to take action – direct action.'

Cohen now knew that he would have to penetrate even deeper into Arab circles. He also knew that it would be more dangerous than before, since all his energies must be spent in identifying the PFLP heads in Europe. And he realized, too, that once terrorist leaders had been pinpointed, he would have to be their executioner.

Thus, in April 1971, a strange manhunt began.

Two men in a chase, each seeking the other, neither knowing very much about his opponent – what his qualities were, what he looked like, or how he operated. Two men of similar age. One born in Israel, the other in Algeria.

Only death could end the double manhunt.

CHAPTER NINE

KILL OR BE KILLED

AT three in the morning of 21st March, 1972, a police patrolman in the Latin Quarter in Paris noticed a grey Citroën GS parked in a strange fashion – as though its owner had abandoned it.

Approaching the car, the gendarme saw that the driver was sitting at the wheel, his head propped up against the windshield. A quick glance was enough. The man was dead. Another corpse lay in the back seat.

Investigation by the Department of Major Felonies quickly revealed that both men had been shot at short range by a 6.35 calibre pistol. They were subsequently identified as Algerians who had arrived in France ten days earlier. Since there was no apparent motive for the double murder, the dossier was marked 'unsolved' and not considered to be of sufficient interest to be brought to the attention of the DST, France's own anti-terrorist department, attached to the Counter Espionage Branch.

This was an administrative blunder.

In fact, the executioner of the two men was a fellow Algerian – none other than Muhamad Boudia.

Boudia had put aside more important matters concerned with his growing Terror International, to take up his old job as an assassin. He knew that the two men had come to France specifically to extract information from him and, in any event, to eliminate him. Thus it was that their corpses ended up in a government morgue.

Boudia was taking no chances.

In fact, Boudia had been expecting trouble for a long time. As he gained in stature as a leader of the PFLP and established himself as an important figure in Marxist revolutionary circles, the Algerian had set in motion a private enterprise plan to encourage an underground in his native land.

As a result of this, money poured into North Africa, and the government in Algiers became thoroughly alarmed. Espionage officers, never renowned for their gentle treatment of suspects at the best of times, quickly wrung from prisoners, under the pressure of crude but effective torture, the revelation that the man Muhamad Boudia was behind the anti-Boumedienne stirrings in their city.

The decision to eliminate Boudia was taken early in 1972.

Two experienced agents, well acquainted with the streets of Paris, were entrusted with this top-level mission.

On the evening of 20th March, 1972, Boudia took a phone call in his office at the theatre. The man on the other end of the line introduced himself as a sympathetic former settler who had just returned from a visit to the land of his birth. He had brought back greetings from Boudia's wife and children, naming the quarter where they lived.

Boudia invited the caller to come and visit him. He apologized for the fact that two evening performances would keep him at the theatre till after midnight, but suggested a rendezvous half an hour after that. The caller did not demur at this unusual hour for a meeting and promised to wait for Boudia outside the theatre in his car.

The car, he said, was a grey Citroën GS.

Years had passed since Boudia had last seen his wife and children, whom he had been forced to leave behind when he fled after the fall of Ben Bella. However, from time to time his most trusted friends had brought him messages and information from the family. Obviously the stranger knew nothing about this – and therein lay the signing of his own death warrant.

Boudia now telephoned Mahmud Hamshari, his trusted lieutenant, and told him to have the Citroen followed. Then, when he put down the phone, he took a gun from its hiding place.

It was a 6.35 calibre pistol. There had been little use for it since his return from Patrice Lumumba University, but from now on it would never leave his side.

At the designated time Boudia found the car waiting for him at the stage door. Without the slightest sign of hesitation or suspicion, he walked over and introduced himself to the driver. They shook hands and then Boudia slid into the vacant seat beside the driver.

'I appreciate your kindness,' Boudia said, 'in coming to see me at this late hour.'

He smiled at the driver. The driver turned the ignition. Then, when the car was moving swiftly along the road, a second man sprang up from the floor behind Boudia and rammed a revolver into his neck.

Boudia didn't move. The car cruised through the streets and the man holding the pistol proposed a deal.

If Boudia would give them the names of his fellow agents in the Algerian underground, he would leave the car unharmed.

Boudia didn't reply immediately. He pretended to think about it. The man tapped his neck with the pistol, menacingly.

'I can give you the names,' Boudia said. 'But how will you know if they're correct? You can't keep me here until you check it. We can't sit here for weeks.'

'Documents,' said the man in the back seat. 'We don't just want the names, we want documentation; we want all your files and correspondence.'

That's what Boudia wanted to hear. He pretended to think about it. He acted like a man who was ashamed, and he spoke with reluctance.

'All right,' he said. 'I'll do it. But you'll have to come to my apartment. I keep all my records in there.'

'That could be a trap,' the man said.

'Right,' Boudia said. 'So it could be a trap. So I give you the keys and one of you goes up and the other one keeps me in the car. It's as simple as that.'

The man agreed. Boudia directed the driver towards the Latin Quarter. It was now ten minutes past one, and it was cold and the streets were quite dark. There was no one about. That was to the good. Then, when they neared Hamshari's apartment, Boudia told them to stop.

'Here,' he said. 'That house over there.'

The driver stopped the car. His companion studied the building. He was checking that it wasn't a trap, just as the terrorist chief had anticipated.

Boudia turned around. He moved very fast. His left hand slammed brutally into the neck of the man behind him while his right hand was whipping out the pistol. Boudia turned back to the driver. The driver hadn't had time to think. The silenced gun coughed, and coughed again, and the driver slumped forward.

Boudia turned to the back again. The man was clutching at his throat. He was gasping and choking and he looked up with wide eyes as Boudia shot him twice in the head. He slumped down and was still.

Boudia climbed out of the car. He wiped his fingerprints from the door handle. Hamshari's car roared out of the darkness and its back door was open. Boudia jumped in. He slammed the door behind him. The car roared along the dark and silent street and was soon lost from view.

The dead Algerians were discovered two hours later.

Apart from an initial burst of exhilaration at having outwitted the 'commando' team sent to kill him, Boudia felt no lasting sense of elation.

He knew that Boumedienne would not take kindly to the loss of two top agents and that others were sure to follow. Clearly he had bothered the Algerian government and now they were after his blood.

He would have to be more careful, and surround himself with bodyguards who knew just what they were doing. He would have to find the best in the business.

Boudia thought immediately of Carlos.

CHAPTER TEN

THE RETURN OF CARLOS

BOUDIA's old friend was working in London.

Shortly after Boudia had moved to Paris, his cover being that of a serious and respected man of the theatre, Carlos had begun to carry out some relatively unimportant missions in the United Kingdom.

The PFLP command, which had been watching him for some time, knew of his ability to change characters like a chameleon; they also knew that despite all the fantasies he wove about himself, Carlos did possess the necessary credentials and background to move freely in any given social circle.

For the time being it was decided to employ Carlos for liaison work and the creation of a PFLP centre in Britain.

He was given sufficient funds to rent a luxurious apartment in Kensington, where he was known as Ilitch Ramirez Sanchez, son of a well-established family from Caracas, Venezuela. The Ramirez Sanchez family had in fact lived many years before in the same district of London, where they had entertained lavishly; now all doors were open to the son.

Neighbours who had known the South Americans were to later tell Scotland Yard investigators that the family, as well as being extremely wealthy, were pleasant and courteous. Their home, with its splendid art collection and antiques, served as a social centre for rich and famous socialites and others from that Latin contingent in the London of the 1960's.

It was recalled that the father, reputed to be a lawyer and a man of property, did not visit his wife and three sons, presumably because his business kept him otherwise occupied. Thus the home was mainly centred on a charming middle-aged woman and three young men. The oldest boy, Vladimir, was then 24 and a student of electronics, sixteen year old Lenin was still at school, and Ilitch did not do much except enjoy life.

All those who knew the family asserted that Ilitch demonstrated all the exaggerated mischievousness of a spoilt child.

His mother was a talented woman, renowned for her broad culture and knowledge of poetry and literature. As a hobby, she collected antiques and knew so much about the subject that other collectors sought her advice. Politically she was vaguely to the left; certainly she seemed to have outgrown her youthful passion for Marxism, for she had named her three sons after Lenin.

The family was close, but there was a particular affection shown by the mother towards her middle son, Ilitch. She always tried to defend him when his pranks got him into trouble, and proudly proclaimed that he was exceptionally talented and that one day the world would recognize his greatness.

If Carlos was indeed Ilitch Ramirez Sanchez, then his mother's prophecy did in fact come true. As the whole world was eventually to discover, he truly did have a rare talent – for murder and terror.

In any event, when the broad-shouldered young man turned up later in London, introducing himself as Ilitch Ramirez Sanchez, there was no reason to doubt his word and he was accepted in Kensington as an old friend who had returned home.

Yet there were people who had known the family who admitted that there were definite changes in the Sanchez boy. They remembered Ilitch as being much thinner, quieter and basically unsure of himself. The older, new-version Ilitch was bold almost to the point of arrogance – and he had certainly filled out in an amazing way.

Nevertheless, he was accepted as Ilitch.

What his neighbours certainly never suspected was that the elegantly furnished apartment was now a guest house for terrorists who, for one reason or another, passed through London.

When word spread among Western security and police forces about the way the Terror International network was flexing its muscles, Scotland Yard sent a report to Interpol that a certain Ilitch Ramirez Sanchez was seen frequently at Heathrow Airport. Their interest in him was aroused by the fact that he was in contact with passengers suspected of affiliation with Arab terrorist groups. The name was unknown however, and the information was simply recorded and placed in an inactive file.

Ilitch proved to be a generous host and his apartment was always full of young men and women. There were frequent parties and it was clear that he was a swinger who enjoyed life to the full and wanted his guests to do the same. He was extremely popular with the ladies, and it was noticed that he possessed an enviable influence over women of all ages. As he put it himself one evening, he knew how to 'keep them simmering over a low flame'.

Yet he was careful not to allow his relationship with any one woman pass beyond a certain point. They usually chased him, but he knew how to handle them, never letting any mistress know he was involved at the same time with several other women.

Once he had established his cover as a rich young man, and was recognized by neighbours as enjoying the company of a wide circle of friends who came and went from his apartment at all hours of the day and night, Carlos grew irritable.

He was more than a little envious of the success and growing prestige of Muhamad Boudia in Paris. Again and again he pressed the PFLP to give him something to do other than set up and keep a 'sleeping cell' in operation in London.

From time to time his apartment acted as a refuge for such terrorists as Leila Khaled, when it was necessary for them to keep out of the limelight; and it was through these personalities that he was able to keep in touch with his old Patrice Lumumba University soul-mate, 'Pierre Guillet'.

Then, as the network took shape and spread its tentacles,

Ilitch Ramirez Sanchez, alias Carlos, was given the task of co-ordinating future mutual assistance between the PFLP and the IRA – for Moscow was now keenly interested in the Irish terror organization, regarding its potential as enormous.

The young man clearly sensed the quickening pulse of events, and his expectations were to prove correct. Sooner than he realized, the fates of 'Carlos' and 'Pierre Guillet' would once more be moving together – this time to be interwoven so finely that only death would ever part them . . .

Six weeks were to elapse before Boudia realized his wish and found himself face to face with Carlos.

First there was a message which arrived from Beirut – a message so important that George Habash sent along the young Michel Mukarbal, fastest rising star in the Palestinian terrorist circle, to deliver it personally to Boudia.

Mukarbal was certainly someone to watch. 'He is talented, reliable and sometimes brilliant,' was the recommendation which had preceded Mukarbal when he had first been brought to the attention of the PFLP leader – and since then Habash had been delighted with the willingness of his lieutenant to obey all orders without question and with dedicated efficiency.

It was Mukarbal who had been entrusted with the task of carrying considerable sums of money to Boudia in Paris. This time, however, he did not bring money. He brought the following message:

'An international freedom fighters' conference has been arranged to take place in the Lebanon shortly. We don't know just where or when, but you should keep yourself available and ready to go at a moment's notice.'

Still feeling his way as a potential successor to Habash, Mukarbal was tactful enough not to issue a direct order to the Algerian, instead converting the first instructions from the PFLP chief into a vague request; but the subtlety of the 'should keep yourself available' was not lost on Boudia.

Early in May, Boudia was indeed summoned to Beirut.

Upon his arrival he found that the conference was scheduled to begin the next morning in Badawi Refugee camp, on the outskirts of Tripoli. This vast, sprawling, slum-like township, housing thousands of Palestinians who had fled from their homeland, had deliberately been chosen as the venue because it was one of the most depressing camps of its kind. It supplied a perfect propaganda backdrop for the rhetoric of the Arab leaders, who were attempting to explain their motives for resorting to violence in achieving their aims. Moreover, no stranger could get near, since the camp was guarded by PFLP personnel, all armed to the teeth.

Boudia had no idea of just how successful the conference organizers had been until he attended the opening session. He was visibly impressed by the vast array of men and women who had flown in from all parts of the world. There were Tupamaros from South America, members of the Turkish Liberation Army, Basques from Spain, Japanese, Irish and Germans – all true freedom fighters who regarded themselves as heroes, even though millions called them terrorists.

George Habash had indeed chosen well.

Badawi Refugee camp was a giant suppurating sore, housing unemployed and desperate people in miserable clay huts interspersed with corrugated iron and wood shanties. The narrow alleyways of raw earth and potholes served as playgrounds for the bands of filthy children dressed in tattered rags.

There were thousands of refugees. Thousands of men, women and children deliberately kept by Arab governments, in misery and degradation, in this camp and others like it around the borders of Israel.

Certainly the oil-rich states had sufficient funds to provide proper homes and jobs for these unfortunate people; but it served them better to exploit the refugees for the purposes of propaganda. Little wonder that after years of idleness and poverty, their meagre resources eked out by aid from UNRWA, the young men in the camps were all too ready to join terrorist groups as the only way out of their apathy and despair.

The Lebanese avoided all contact with the refugees in their country, and Badawi was no exception. Lebanese Army

93

units and Christian Falangists kept their distance from the area, leaving it entirely under the control of the terrorist movements. This was a costly mistake on the part of the wealthy citizens of this Mediterranean country, since the camps proved such a festering sore that they were to be the cause of civil war which rent the country in two in 1975, and total chaos in the following year.

In full view of Badawi was the rich metropolis of Tripoli, second largest city in the Lebanon. A beautiful city. A port through which oil flowed to the distant countries of Europe. The comparison between their own wretched poverty and the affluence of Tripoli and its well-off citizens, who shunned the Palestinians like the plague, was a bitter taste in the throats of the refugees.

Mukarbal wanted Boudia to seek accommodation with the other senior 'freedom fighters' in a stone house belonging to the PFLP at the east end of the refugee area, but to his astonishment Boudia insisted on checking into a hotel in Tripoli.

Seeing the surprise on Mukarbal's face, Boudia merely said that it had something to do with his childhood, but declined to elaborate any further. Thus, after a quick tour of the camp – to let Boudia see for himself just how it was with his suffering Palestinian brothers – the aide dropped Boudia at a comfortable hotel on the sea front.

'I'll come back for you at eight,' Mukarbal said. 'Habash wants to meet you and a few others.'

Boudia wanted some time alone to reflect on what he had seen. The tour of the camp had not been an easy experience. He unpacked his bags, then went out to the terrace overlooking the sea and sank back into an easy chair. The sun was already beginning to sink, flooding the waters of the Mediterranean with a golden glow. The Algerian watched giant oil tankers swinging at anchor outside the oil port and thought of what he had seen that afternoon.

Badawi had shocked him.

Poverty and cramped conditions, the stench and hunger, and, above all, the hopelessness ... all took him back many years to his own unhappy childhood in a desolate, impoverished Algerian village. It was almost as if time had stood still, leaving him drained.

After this traumatic experience, Boudia's work with the Popular Front would acquire a whole new dimension. Suddenly, freeing Algeria could wait. These people were Arabs – Arabs whose Palestinian home had been taken from them. And now, for the first time in his life, Boudia hated the Jews. For the first time since joining the PFLP he was ready to commit himself wholeheartedly to their cause, no matter where it might lead.

He, Muhamad Boudia, would slaughter the Jews.

Habash was happy with what he saw, though his stiff features gave no outward sign of it. He was sitting behind a long table, a map of Palestine above his head, surveying the high level group of selected senior men who had gathered for the evening in his command post on the edge of Badawi Camp.

His eyes lit up when he spotted the bearded face of Abu Iyad. That crafty associate of Habash's rival, Yasir Arafat, would one day openly transfer his allegiance to Habash. Iyad was seated alongside Farhi el-Omri, who would later take his place in the bloody pages of terror history as the commander of the massacre at the Munich Olympics. Further down the table was Habash's own Chief of Operations, Dr. Wadi Hadad, a man of bold and inventive mind. Also present was his representative in Cyprus, Hussein Bashir, and Michel Mukarbal, Habash's most valued assistant. Surrounding the group was a bodyguard of six young men, all heavily armed to protect this valuable and experienced assembly.

Habash had brought these men together so that they could hear his plans for forthcoming operations, many of which would only become possible as a result of their presence at this meeting.

He opened with a survey of the preceding six months, devoting more time to the successes than to the disasters, which he merely glossed over. His audience was well aware of the widening gap between himself and Arafat's el-Fatah organization, but Habash spoke with a self-confidence which sprang from the knowledge that he had proved to be more dangerous to the Israelis than the blustering Arafat.

'We are happy at the prospect of operating in concert with other freedom movements,' Habash said. He then listed the various organizations that had sent delegates to the founding session of the 'Leftist Freedom Fighters' International' and concluded: 'I am going to call on you all to assist in delivering heavy blows to Israel.'

Now the tension grew, because Habash was obviously about to announce a major change of tactics and a vital fruit to be plucked by their presence in Badawi that day.

'I have undertakings,' Habash finally said, 'that the various movements in different countries, in return for financial and material aid from us, will carry out strikes within the heart of Israel. We have the backing from certain Arab countries for the groups that will co-operate with us.'

Habash then spelt out the guidelines of the coming joint efforts, and Boudia listened attentively, for here was tangible expression of that long-range plan devised by KGB experts and outlined for him in Moscow.

At the close of the meeting Boudia was asked to stay on for a private conversation with Habash. It wasn't his first tête-à-tête with the PFLP chief, and the two men greeted each other with smiles and the traditional kissing on both cheeks.

'This is quite an event,' Boudia said, referring to the previous proceedings.

'Thank you,' Habash said. 'It wasn't easy to organize.'

Soon the conversation took a turn which made the Algerian's ears prick up in anticipation.

'We are planning to shock the enemy,' Habash said.

'An operation in Israel?' Boudia asked.

Habash refused to go into details, but added: 'It is really a matter for discussion between myself and Furoy Yutaka, who is here as a personal representative of Fusaku Shiganovu. I know you have already met him in Paris. He speaks highly of you. And it is because of this excellent relationship you have established with him that I am going to entrust you with a very important task. I am making you responsible

for all the background assistance that has to be given to the
Red Army men who are leading the assault. You will need
money and more men for this purpose. You will get everything you need from us.'

Habash stood up and walked to the door. Mukarbal, who
had brought Boudia to the meeting, was still waiting patiently in the darkened ante-room. Habash nodded his head and
Mukarbal disappeared. Habash returned to the low couch.

'I have asked Michel to call a man who I think can be
helpful to you,' he said. 'Check him out. If you want him,
fine. If not, you will have to find the right man yourself.'

The door opened and Mukarbal appeared. There could be
no mistaking the man who stood behind him in the gloom.
Boudia smiled.

'Hello, Carlos!' he said.

CHAPTER ELEVEN

BLOOD FOR BLOOD

THE reunion between Boudia and Carlos was cut short unexpectedly at 5 in the morning.

Until that hour they sat on the balcony of the Algerian's bedroom, filling in the gaps since they had last met and warmly relating their recent experiences. Mutual respect, warmth and an almost brotherly love kept them both up all night.

Only one subject was taboo: Nicole. Both knew that she had flitted from one to the other since those early days at Patrice Lumumba University, but not once was she mentioned, not even by the slightest allusion.

The sun was now rising, throwing a crimson glow of impending warmth across the fading night sky.

Then they heard an immense peal of thunder.

The hotel windows shook as the sound echoed and reverberated around them. They both jumped to their feet. Westward, two threatening shadows flew low over the port and on towards Badawi Camp.

They raced to the end of the terrace, where they could see what was happening. Just as they did so, the building shook from the blast of two more explosions. They saw a glow in the distance.

'Badawi Camp!' Carlos shouted. 'Israelis!'

Angry, frustrated, the two friends watched the metallic glitter of the aircraft as they flashed through the rays of the rising sun. Gigantic smoke mushrooms were spiralling to the dawn sky. A volcanic glow was reaching up through the pearly air. The Phantom jets, their engines shrieking insanely, made another low run over the general area of the PFLP headquarters.

More bombs fell. The thunder emanated from the camp and resounded across the city of Tripoli. Smoke plumes spouted, one after the other, in an oblique line across the target area. And now there was the sound of gunfire. Machine-guns and rifles. The men in the camp were firing at the planes, hopelessly, furiously, with everything they could get their hands on.

Suddenly the Phantoms vanished into the silvery-grey clouds, leaving silence and a pulsating, fiery smoke.

Minutes later Boudia and Carlos were hurtling in the car down the road to Badawi. They were still some distance away when already they heard the shouting and demented wailing of the refugees. Then the car bounced and lurched into the camp.

Gangs of children were setting fire to piles of tyres, adding more smoke to the black clouds billowing over the camp. Whole rows of shanties had collapsed or had been blown apart, now nothing but ugly heaps of rubble, the wood scorched and smouldering. Men and women were wandering around, weeping and wailing, still dazed by the speed and savagery of the attack.

They met Habash in the courtyard. He was surrounded by bodyguards and other delegates. He was pacing up and down like a wounded tiger, pointing at the damage, cursing Israel and the Israelis. His guests watched in silence. They didn't dare interrupt. And the events of the last few minutes had told them all they needed to know about the nature of this particular Middle-East conflict.

Suddenly the air was rent by desperate screams.

They all looked around. Beyond the barbed wire that surrounded the command post, a crowd of refugees were dragging the writhing figure of a man. Others were striking at him with sticks. Women were running behind, wailing hyterically, trying to heave huge stones at the unfortunate captive.

'Kill him!' they shrieked. 'Death to traitors!'

The group in the compound stood watching as the victim

99

was dragged to a wooden post in the gap between two alleys and then lashed to it with thick ropes. The man was writhing and shouting. He was obviously terrified. More spectators were rushing in from all directions, while children rolled burning tyres into a giant circle that obscured the scene with acrid black smoke.

Moments before the plane attack, Hassan Sheloub, a refugee just like any other, had been seen to light a bonfire near the command post. It required little imagination for the mob to believe that he had been guilty of guiding the planes to their target. Now Sheloub's terrified protestations that he had simply been baking bread for his family were in vain. He was beaten. He was lashed to the posts. He was kicked and spat upon.

Half-demented, Sheloub watched the mob closing in on him. He screamed for mercy. His screams were ignored. His body was struck again and again by stones. Smoking strips of rubber were flung at his feet. Lumps of dried dung were pounded into his face. His screaming was drowned out by the wailing of the women who now danced around him as if in some strange religious rite.

There was a rubber hose attached to a faucet at the side of a nearby shack. A man grabbed the hose and turned on the tap, while another seized Sheloub's head and forced his mouth open. Sheloub screamed. The screaming stopped abruptly as the hose was rammed down his throat and the sudden flow of water distended his skinny frame. He exploded and died.

The barbaric execution of an innocent man seemed to console and satisfy the mob. Their rage now gave way to primitive howls of joy.

None of the men around Habash had done anything to save the victim – even though their word was law in the camp.

Water was still flowing into and through Sheloub's body as, with a final twitch, his limbs ceased their frantic shuddering and his head lolled over to the side. His eyes turned upwards, the dead white reflecting the sun's rays. A pool of water collected at his feet. He just hung there. A wet rag.

The horror of the day was treated by George Habash as a heaven-sent gift to his conference.

Five hundred yards from the camp a field had been cleared to make way for a military-style tent camp. The delegates were brought here a few minutes after 9.00 a.m. Refugees from the camp lined the approach road, waving flags emblazoned with the symbol of the Popular Front for the Liberation of Palestine. As the cars moved slowly in a long line, they were greeted by ecstatic, fanatical cries:

'Falastin! Falastin! Falastin!'

Once inside the camp, the delegates saw groups of men of all ages, ranging from boys of thirteen to middle-aged veterans, methodically engaged in their training exercises.

It was a deliberately staged propaganda operation.

Nevertheless, the delegates were impressed; and seated in a large hut at the camp centre, the foreigners were emotionally ripe for George Habash's speech. He did not let them down.

'Brothers!'

The word with which the PFLP leader opened the founding session of the Freedom Fighters' International was to be repeated at the beginning or end of almost every sentence. This was a different George Habash. No longer the restrained and thoughtful chairman of internal meetings, he drew on his full arsenal of colourful rhetoric to paint his own vision of the destruction of the Jewish State.

'Brothers! No stone will be left unturned! Nothing will escape us! Nothing will evade us! The bodies of the Jews will be flung into the sea!'

He threatened. He cajoled. He caressed and he whipped. He spoke of the brotherhood of men fighting to create a new world, of a pure and progressive social regime . . .

'There is no other way, brothers! The old world must be destroyed! The new will be built on its ruins!'

He spoke for an hour. The applause was thunderous. The ovation lasted for several minutes. Then, before Furoya Yutaka, the last of the foreign orators, stepped up, Pedro Zolar, the Tupamaros representative, had his turn:

'It is not by mere words that we shall contribute. It is not by mere words that we shall tip the world over on its face. Only by deeds! Actions that will shock our enemies and glorify us! We must continue working, stage by stage, each in his own place. And we must do our best to help our Palestinian brothers. May all of you be blessed by the God in whom you believe!'

Blood. Lust for blood that was soon to have its passion sated. The cry for blood now sounded like a crazed obsession – a madness that was bringing the whole world closer to a grim chasm of violence heaped upon more violence.

This new dawn was breaking.

PART THREE:

THE SWORD AND THE FLAME

CHAPTER TWELVE

MASSACRE AT LOD AIRPORT

BOUDIA would never forget that he was a partner in, and a patron of, the first great international terrorist bloodbath. Carlos would remember it as one of the most sublime and inspiring moments of his career.

The Lod Airport massacre was the first real fruit of the terrifying alliance between the terrorist groups, and the brainchild of the Soviet's plan to exploit their relationship with them in building up a groundswell of violence.

The Japanese were quick to prove that the Red Army did not deal in words alone, were in fact the first to show the world that the festival of death was expanding its boundaries.

Boudia received his orders to assist the Oriental team a few days after the Badawi conference. The assistance given by Boudia and Carlos would be vital; and this was Carlos's great moment, his first real opportunity to be a partner in an impressive prestige operation.

Their first duty was to act as hosts to the Japanese team when they arrived in Europe from Tokyo, on their way to carry out their suicide mission.

Israel's security services were in a high state of alert, but none of the men responsible could have conceived an operation quite as diabolical as the one worked out between Dr. George Habash and the Red Army.

In addition, this was the first operation against Israel to be cloaked in absolute silence from the first stages of planning to the last. Not one word about it reached Israeli ears, apart from a very general hint that there could be some form of co-operation between Palestinian terrorists and their Japanese partners.

Meanwhile, Boudia was performing his duties methodically, and in an unparalleled aura of secrecy. Carlos proved an admirable partner; and it was thanks to the previously-established links with the Baader-Meinhof gang that he was able to get the Japanese killers across Europe without any leaks to the agents of several countries now on the watch for internationally-organized terrorism.

Boudia was also responsible for training the Japanese team, which in this instance meant briefing on the scene of their operation and co-ordination of a rapidly unfolding time-table.

The attack was set for 30th May, 1972.

Boudia and Carlos were now working so smoothly as a team that the Algerian did not even tell his former right-hand man, Mahmud Hamshari, what was going on. Besides, the fewer let into the secret, the less chance of a security leak.

Forged passports were prepared under Boudia's careful eye. It was Carlos who was given the task of taking the necessary weapons to Rome, where security was sufficiently ill-organized to enable the Japanese to take them aboard an Air France plane to Israel.

During the last week of May, the Japanese kamikaze team were the guests of Baader-Meinhof. On the 29th, they crossed the borders into Italy, on their way to Rome. Once in the Italian capital, they were lodged in a private apartment to avoid any unnecessary suspicion.

On Tuesday, 30th May, 1972, Boudia went through his normal daily routine. He worked in the theatre, then spent the evening with a group of actors, discussing the repertoire for the coming summer season. He left them close to midnight, and returned to his apartment in the Latin Quarter.

Sipping from a large mug of coffee, Boudia sprawled on the bed. He switched on the radio seconds before midnight and, as he waited for the news bulletin, continued studying a copy of Jean Genet's *The Balcony*, which he intended to produce the following year.

The midnight news carried the item he had been waiting for: a report of a massacre at Lod International Airport. The announcer also noted that the Popular Front for the Liberation of Palestine had just published a communique claiming responsibility for the operation.

Boudia was now tense and expectant. Clearly his squad had succeeded beyond all expectations. But he had to wait several hours before the grim details were spelt out . . .

The night of Tuesday, 30th May, 1972, was a routine if busy one for the staff at Lod. Planes were landing one after the other, carrying hundreds of tourists and pilgrims, all visiting the Holy Land in the full bloom of spring. The police on passport control and the porters in the Customs Hall were under heavy pressure, for as one plane-load of passengers left the terminal building, more poured in to take their place.

It was therefore hardly surprising that after so many routine landings nobody paid any particular attention to the Air France arrival, now offloading passengers from Paris and Rome.

Soon these passengers were milling around the conveyor belts, waiting for their luggage – mostly Puerto Rican pilgrims and a few returning Israelis.

Also, three Japanese – small and inconspicuous – standing quietly together.

Suitcases from the flight began to appear on the moving belt. Here and there, passengers were pouncing on their own luggage. A few of the luckier ones hurried through customs – not knowing that fate was sparing their lives.

The Japanese were bending over their suitcases. Then suddenly they straightened up. They were holding Kalachnikov carbines and hand grenades.

The whole place went crazy.

As the first shots ripped through the closed hall and the first grenades exploded, nobody quite realized what was happening. The noise was appalling. People started to scream. More hand grenades exploded and hurled bodies against walls, over chairs. The noise echoed and reverberated. The chaos was total. There were more screams and people were falling, kicking legs, waving arms.

The Japanese worked with horrifying efficiency.

Bullets criss-crossed the floor in a satanic dance. More hand grenades exploded. People ran left and right, blindly searching for escape before falling down riddled with pain. Others dived under tables, behind luggage, behind chairs, behind the desks of the Ministry of Tourism officials who were stunned by it all. The guns continued to roar. The hand grenades exploded. Hit by bullets, torn by shrapnel, people tumbled to the floor and lay still, sometimes twitching, groaning and shrieking, their blood flowing across the cool tiles ...

The first security men to reach the spot were Border Police accompanied by a few civilian police officers. Drawing their revolvers, they added to the uproar, now answering bullet for bullet.

One of the Japanese held a hand grenade. It exploded before he threw it, tearing his head off.

The second killer strayed into his comrade's line of fire and he, too, died.

The third ran to escape, and was caught.

Calls went out for ambulances. Hospitals across central Israel were alerted for a full-scale emergency. Doctors were called urgently to their wards and operating theatres. The sound of sirens split the night as more police and medical teams converged on the crowded, stricken airport.

The passenger hall resembled a charnel house.

The dead and the wounded were rushed to Tel Hashomer, Ichilov, Beilinson and Assaph Harofeh Hospitals, where, in the early hours of the morning, the full scope of the tragedy was ascertained.

Twenty-eight dead and seventy wounded – some of whom were to die later.

Most of those who had perished were Puerto Rican pilgrims who had no connection whatsoever with Israel. Among the Israeli dead was Professor Aharon Katzir, a world-renowned scientist and head of the Weizman Institute's Department of Polymer Chemistry. He was fifty-nine years of age, a man in his intellectual prime. His brother, Ephraim Katzir, also a professor at Weizmann, was destined to be the next President of Israel.

At dawn, security officers stood at the doors of the passenger hall, looking at the aftermath of the night of violence.

Pools of blood were drying in dull brown stains on the floor. Pieces of human flesh were stuck to suitcases and furniture. Bags had been torn open, clothes ripped to shreds. Here and there, abandoned childrens' toys lay on the ground. A tiny doll, its legs and arms blown off, remained as a silent memorial to the dead child carried out not long before ...

In this same grey dawn Deputy Prime Minister Yigal Allon was facing the batteries of microphones of the Israeli and overseas media. His face was pale, and his words attempted to express the inexpressible:

'This is an act of horror of which only madmen would be capable. In the whole Arab world there wasn't one man who would agree to perpetuate an act tantamount to suicide, so they had to hire Japanese to do it for them. It isn't even possible to express the scale of our pain and anger ...'

They were Japanese. Three diminutive Japanese. Inconspicuous, ordinary-looking men. They were also Shiganovu's Red Army gunmen, to whom Israel meant nothing at all. They were kamikaze killers sent to carry out a massacre, and they had no deeper interest in it than that.

Interrogation of the surviving member of the suicide team was progressing fast. His name was Kozo Okamoto, but he did not know the real names of his companions. He only knew the name of the man from the Arab terrorist organization that had trained and protected them in Europe.

Hector Hippodikon.

The Japanese killer had been told that Hippodikon was of mixed French-English parentage; but he did point out that Hippodikon spoke with an accent which had to be either Arab or South American. Kozo Okamoto knew no more than that, but he did finally add a few more details about the man: Hippodikon was between twenty-five and his early thirties.

Within minutes this sparse description was being relayed to scores of Israeli agents across Europe, with the instruction that they were to find him whoever he was.

In fact, he was Carlos.

A few minutes after nine in the morning, Boudia received a phone call from London – one for which he had been waiting impatiently.

'Thanks for the birthday present,' Carlos said.

'I'll be happy to send one like it every year,' Boudia replied.

Boudia hung up the phone. Now he could relax. Carlos, who had looked after the team when in Europe, had returned safely from Rome to London. It was time to lie low for a while.

The Algerian couldn't sleep. He picked up Genet's play. At first he couldn't concentrate, but eventually he got into it, and soon he was lost in Genet's black world.

Once again, Boudia was a man of the theatre, an intellectual utterly absorbed by the drama of the written word, the blood and the ruin forgotten.

Truly, he was the king of two stages.

CHAPTER THIRTEEN

A CLEAN DEATH

KHADER KANO, a Syrian journalist representing Radio Damascus, had been in Paris for some time. He was most noticeable for his life-style and his knowledge of the city. He seemed to have limitless funds – though nobody knew where the money came from – and certainly no other reporter in the French capital dressed as well, drove such an expensive car, or lived in a luxurious apartment in the 18th arrondisement.

Kano was considered brilliant at his job and was known to have valuable sources of information. His thorough knowledge of the corridors of power, and intimacy with its practitioners, gave him a decided advantage over his Arab colleagues. Furthermore, he was welcome in Arab extremist circles in Paris, where he was renowned for his fervour regarding the Palestinian cause. In fact, Kano was only too eager to tell anyone who would listen of the vital need to wipe the Jewish State off the map. All in all, he presented the definitive image of a fiery Arab nationalist.

Because Kano's journalistic activities had opened many doors into the complex hierarchy of French government, he picked up items of information that could be very important for the terrorist organizations – and he was not at all averse to proving his worth to the PFLP. Indeed, from time to time he gave such details to Mahmud Hamshari, and much of this information had to do with the activities of the anti-terror department of counter espionage: the DST.

Boudia had often heard Hamshari mention Khader Kano.

His deputy was unsparing in his praise of the Syrian and the assistance he was giving to the European network.

'He wants to meet you,' Hamshari said one day to Boudia.

Boudia stared at him. 'He knows of my existence?' he asked.

Hamshari smiled. 'You could say that nothing about us,' he said, 'large or small, escapes his notice.'

'Interesting,' Boudia said, looking calm, feeling alarmed. 'I assume that he needs information *about* us, so that he can judge just what sort of information to get *for* us?'

'Exactly.' Hamshari smiled. 'And that's why he wants to meet you. They were almost his exact words. He would like to hear from you personally which sources of information would be of interest in the future.'

'Precisely what does he know about me?' Boudia asked.

'Not much,' Hamshari replied. 'Only that I report to nobody else.'

Boudia knew Kano's reputation. He had seen him a few times at the theatre. In his own view the glib Syrian was just too good to be true. Hamshari had got to the top in the organization through deep loyalty and unquestioning obedience; but as Boudia knew, he was not exactly endowed with too much intelligence. Clearly he had not even begun to suspect that a man like Kano could be a very real danger to the network.

The open struggle between the Mossad and the terror organizations had recently been picking up in intensity. It was now clear that the Israelis were resolved to use any means of getting at the senior command echelons. The situation had been growing steadily worse since the Japanese operation at Lod Airport, and the latest terrorist successes were obviously infuriating the Israelis.

Their security forces were further shocked by the murder of eleven Israeli sportsmen at the Olympic Games in Munich, 9th September, 1972.

The conversation between Boudia and Hamshari about Khader Kano took place only three days after the Munich affair. Boudia was, at this time, especially sensitive to the possibility of Israeli retaliation. And worrying rumours of someone inside the network systematically leaking information to the Israelis only served to sharpen his sensitivity.

Had it not been for Kano's pressing desire to meet Boudia – though at this stage the Syrian did not know the Algerian's name – Carlos might not have been summoned from his dormant cell in London. However, within three hours of Hamshari's disturbing news, the Algerian had phoned his double in London ...

At noon that same day, Carlos was recorded, when passing through Passport Control at Heathrow, London, as holding documents in the name of Carlos Andreas Martinez, a Columbian citizen born on 4th May, 1947. A few hours later, Carlos Andreas Martinez was sitting in the darkened theatre where Boudia worked.

He was given a thumb-nail sketch of Khader Kano and the Algerian's suspicions concerning the 36-year-old Syrian. Boudia told Carlos that he suspected the Syrian of being a double agent. He wanted Carlos to put him under surveillance.

'The Israelis have been using fresh methods recently,' Boudia said. 'Since we have been more careful about our own men, they are finding it increasingly difficult to get information on planned operations. This has left them only one option: the elimination of our top field commanders. Stage one: they have to identify us. And for that they are buying informers, in and around us, for sizeable sums.'

'All right,' Carlos said. 'If Khader Kano turns out to be a double agent – then what?'

'You know what,' Boudia said. 'He will have to vanish.'

Carlos was pleased. This was the first time that Boudia had exposed him to this kind of work; it implied that Boudia was now trusting him sufficiently to let him enter the real arena of active duty. He had waited a long time for this and it filled him with pleasure.

'I can't rely on my own men,' Boudia continued. 'Not for this job. But you're unknown to him. You can operate without interference. I want you to hang on to Khader Kano and not let him out of your sight. You have open expenses. Take as long as you like. But I want to know the truth about this man. I expect good results.'

'You will get them,' Carlos said.

Shortly after parting from Boudia, Carlos checked into a hotel on the Rue de Lambert. Boudia had told him that Hamshari's current mistress lived in this street – and if Kano was tailing Hamshari he would turn up here sooner or later. From that point on, Carlos would follow him wherever he went.

The new guest in the Rue de Lambert was very fussy. He insisted on a second-floor room in the front of the hotel. He said he was not to be interrupted. He was polite, but firm.

It did not take long. In fact, that very same night, as Carlos sat at the window, Boudia's fears were confirmed in a dramatic fashion.

At one in the morning, Carlos saw Hamshari coming out of the building across the street and walking towards his parked car. Suddenly, a dark-coloured Peugeot 404 darted towards the Arab. Three shots were fired at him, but missed their mark. The Peugeot gathered speed and vanished. Eventually Hamshari straightened up from behind his own vehicle. The only damage done was a shattered wing mirror.

Two men reported the incident to Boudia: Hamshari and Carlos. But Hamshari, unaware of Carlos's presence in Paris, only told his chief in the morning. Boudia remained silent about the fact that he had already received full details from Carlos.

Hamshari now knew that he was a marked man; but he couldn't think who had identified him to the Israelis. Consequently, he surrounded himself with bodyguards.

Carlos continued his surveillance of Khader Kano.

'You must find out who his contacts are,' Boudia said. 'It is of vital importance.'

Carlos tailed Kano for a week, after which time he could reconstruct with precision his every move. The Syrian journalist was indeed an active man. He was meeting people from morning to night – his professional colleagues, DST officers, members of the terrorist groups – a colourful, but seemingly innocent social round.

Then, on the seventh day of the hunt, Boudia lost contact with Carlos – and it was twenty-four hours before his young double resurfaced. Contact came in the form of a brief telephone call:

'You were right,' Carlos said.

An hour later, Boudia and Carlos sat together in the empty theatre where Carlos recounted his story.

On the evening of Monday, two days previously, Carlos had been sitting in the Café Select in Montparnasse, watching Khader Kano who was in another corner of the café in the company of some friends – all French, all sons and daughters of well-to-do families. Carlos thought he noticed some tension on the face of the Syrian; he also noticed that Kano glanced frequently at his watch. Obviously he was waiting for something.

At nine o'clock, precisely, the café doors opened and a man came in and carefully looked around him as if he was searching for someone. Noticing Khader Kano, he turned on his heel and left. A minute or two later, the Syrian parted from his guests and also left the café.

Carlos followed him.

He saw the journalist walk along the street as far as a small restaurant that sold, from a front window stall, takeaway portions of sausage and chips. Kano stopped to make a purchase, and while he was waiting for his portion, the second man walked up to him.

The two men traded envelopes; then, without a word, the second man walked away.

Carlos didn't hesitate. He followed the new quarry. The trail led eventually from Paris to Brussels and right up to the front door of the Israel Embassy.

At this point, Carlos returned to Paris to report his findings to Boudia. And when he had finished his story, Boudia said simply:

'Kill him. But cleanly. No beatings, no torture. I'll take care of the Israeli myself.'

Boudia knew exactly who had to be eliminated in the Israel Embassy in Brussels; he therefore summoned one of his men who was acquainted with Belgium, gave him instructions, and sent him on his way. Meanwhile, Carlos went about his own task.

The following day Carlos phoned Boudia again.

'The temperature is down,' he announced.

'Good,' Boudia said. 'Go home . . . and a fast recovery.'

Again, it was time for Carlos to lie low. But, as he was pleased to discover, his inactivity was not to last very long . . .

Kano's death was only discovered a day or two later when his neighbours complained to the local police about a pungent odour coming from the Syrian's locked apartment.

A patrol dispatched to the building had to break down the door to get in. Inside, they were greeted by a powerful stench. The rotting body of Khader Kano was lying on the carpet in the luxurious salon. A post-mortem report revealed that three bullets from a pistol had pierced his heart.

The ballistics report indicated 9mm cartridges from an automatic, but the police investigators could not identify the type of gun used. All they could do was note that the job had been done by a master marksman who had obviously entered the apartment with a passkey and waited for his victim to come home.

The dossier was handed over to the DST who filed it under 'conflicts between various factions of Arab terror'.

Boudia's second messenger of death was not quite so successful. A report in the Belgian papers stated that Zadok Ophir, an employee of the Israeli Embassy, had been shot a few times while walking in a main street of Brussels. He was badly injured, but would eventually recover.

From Boudia's point of view it was a double miss. The still-alive Ophir wasn't even the man he had wanted to eliminate . . .

CHAPTER FOURTEEN

THE HUNTER

THE three shots fired at Mahmud Hamshari, senior representative of the PFLP – the assassination attempt witnessed by Carlos – marked a dramatic turning point in the game of life and death in the Paris terror area that September night.

As Hamshari straightened up slowly from behind his car, he felt his heart beating wildly. This was the first time since his arrival in France that he had found himself exposed directly to the men who wanted to kill him. It was an unhappy moment.

But for Hamshari the situation was even more serious than he imagined. Without being fully aware of it, Hamshari had been granted the rather dubious honour of being the first to know that Israel had foreclosed on the truce forced upon her in Paris by the French authorities and had opened a new front against her enemies. A front that would henceforth recognize no borders.

Certainly the public could not suspect that the streets of Paris were shortly to become an arena of death in which various espionage services would strike at the operatives of the growing Terror International. The DST, whose job it was on behalf of the French Counter-Espionage Service to avert just such a battle, had so far done nothing more than keep their fingers crossed. Their hope was that both sides would act in a gentlemanly way and not spill each other's blood in *La Belle France*.

But dramatic events were about to unfold. For the Israel

security chiefs ordered a sudden and extreme change of tactics following the massacre at Lod.

Golda Meir, then Prime Minister of Israel, declared after the murder of the twenty-eight men, women and children at the airport:

'From now on, Israel will wage a war of annihilation against the murderers. We will strike at them everywhere, with skill and courage. Fatal blows.'

A few months passed and it gradually became clear that the declaration of Israel's ageing lioness spelt death for operatives in the terror groups.

And Mahmud Hamshari was high on the 'death' list.

The Arab knew that the first attempt on his life was not the end of a chapter, but rather the opening of a new and more dangerous period for him. Thus, for his protection he had enlisted from among his network several well-trained 'gorillas' to keep an alert watch night and day on his apartment in the Latin Quarter and to shadow him wherever he went. Now, even when he called at his mistress's home, a man stood on guard outside her apartment while three others kept watch in the street below. His personal security arrangements were carefully vetted by Boudia himself, as Hamshari was a highly respected man in terrorist circles.

However, Hamshari made the mistake of believing that the Israelis could no longer get at him. But his enemies were determined to do just that – and to carry out the task they chose a young man with special talents for 'annihilation' actions.

This lone assassin arrived in Paris in November of that year and, from the moment he passed through Orly Airport, he began methodically to plan the elimination of Mahmud Hamshari.

After a few weeks, in which he worked totally independent of any other Israeli agent, he had finalized his arrangements.

He knew it was not going to be easy. He also knew he could do it.

Now the lone killer set in motion, calmly and meticulously, the various steps needed to complete his mission . . .

The tenants in the building alongside Mahmud Hamshari's apartment were not particularly surprised or curious when, one morning early in December, an elderly plumber appeared in their courtyard. The faucet had been dripping for quite a while and everybody assumed that some public-spirited neighbour had sent for a plumber to put it right.

The slow-moving plumber took the tap apart, and found a leak in a stretch of the main conduit. For this reason he had to dismantle the old pipe, which required going into the next-door courtyard, since the pipe served both buildings.

The stocky, surly Arab who stood guard at the entrance of Hamshari's apartment block stopped the plumber from entering the courtyard and regarded him with the utmost suspicion. He listened to the plumber's explanation, told him to wait while he checked the other building, went off and returned, satisfied.

Quickly losing interest in the plumber's laborious struggle with the water pipes, the bodyguard went back to the more agreeable pastime of watching the girls go by.

Half an hour later, the plumber left the courtyard, taking with him a four-metre length of damaged pipe. He soon returned with a new piece, and this time, the guard completely ignored him. By noon, the plumber had finished assembling the section in the yard and had replaced another piece under the pavement itself, this time in the stretch between the stone wall of the building and the kerb.

The bored bodyguard did not notice that the plumber was also working close to the cables carrying the telephone wires. Consequently he did not see that an alien wire had been attached to the line that led into Hamshari's apartment.

This new wire was buried alongside the freshly installed water pipe next door. It carried on under the wall of the building and ended up at the kerbstone.

The plumber had done a sound job. He collected his tools, stowed them in his bag, took a swig of *vin ordinaire* from the bottle he had brought along with him, and politely offered some to the bodyguard. The bodyguard refused and the plumber, with a shrug, went on his way.

Next morning, there were disturbing sounds of static on

Hamshari's telephone. Calls were cut off suddenly, and other voices interfered as he kept getting crossed lines. At first, Hamshari thought it was no more than a passing technical fault, but when the problem had persisted for two days, he lost patience and called the Post Office.

Neither Hamshari nor his bodyguard guessed that the interference on the line had anything to do with the plumber or a Peugeot laundry van, bearing the name of a well-known local firm, that was now parked several times a day in front of the neighbouring building.

Neither did anyone notice that a telephone wire ran up from the kerb and into the van, where it was connected to an electronic device that gave the young driver absolute control over Hamshari's telephone.

It was this young man who was causing all the interference with the calls to and from the PFLP's distressed representative. Now all he had to do was wait for the inevitable call to the exchange – and at noon on Wednesday his patience was rewarded.

The young man lifted his receiver the moment he heard the dialling tone. He listened in silence. Hamshari asked for Telephone Maintenance, and the young man promptly cut the call, then waited, calm but expectant. A few seconds later, exactly as he had anticipated, he heard the dialling tone again. He lifted the receiver.

'Exchange,' he announced in a perfect Parisian accent.

'Monsieur,' Hamshari said in an angry, guttural Middle Eastern voice, 'for some days my telephone hasn't been working properly. I'm getting constant interference, cut calls. Only a moment ago, when I was trying to contact you, even that call was cut off . . .'

The man at the 'Exchange' told Hamshari that they would send someone around, but that it would have to wait until the following week. Hamshari exploded, and insisted that he needed the phone for his business and couldn't tolerate the interference any longer.

'All right, monsieur,' the 'Exchange' said. 'We'll send an engineer tomorrow morning.'

That Wednesday night, the first in December, Paris was

treated to a snowfall. Indeed the snow had arrived so late that optimists had been assuring their friends that it was going to be a mild winter. The snow fell. It settled quietly.

At eight o'clock the following morning, a bearded individual reported to the apartment of Mahmud Hamshari and said that he had come to fix the telephone. The bodyguard saw a government telephone van parked at the kerb, so he only made a cursory examination of the technician's bag. This process was repeated, with equal brevity, by the two 'gorillas' at the entrance to the apartment. Nobody suspected that the technician was also the 'plumber' who had previously worked in the courtyard.

'I have to go out for a few minutes,' Hamshari said when the technician had entered the apartment. 'I'll be back shortly.'

'Fine, sir,' the 'technician' said. 'I should be through by then.'

Hamshari left. The technician was as good as his word. He finished half an hour later, told the guards that the phone was repaired, and then left.

The telephone van drove away. Twenty minutes later, the plumber-technician returned. He was now a fresh-faced young man. The beard had disappeared. The clothes were different and he wore heavy-rimmed spectacles. He walked into Madame Tarpieux's café and ordered coffee and a fresh buttered roll.

It was precisely 9.25 a.m.

So far, everything was on schedule. The young man had just settled down to his breakfast when two Peugeot 404's drove up and parked opposite. The Arab bodyguard remained in the white Peugeot while Mahmud Hamshari and an attractive, straight-backed blonde climbed out of the yellow vehicle and vanished hurriedly through the stone gateway of the building facing the café.

The young man in the café watched them idly. He slowly ate his roll and drank his coffee. He looked frail, studious – one of those romantic, dreamy students who are forever lost in a world of poetry, a million miles away from the rough and tumble of everyday life. Nothing special. A pale, academic young man.

Meanwhile, the snow came drifting down ...

At that moment France was busy with its own affairs and generally unconcerned with the tentacles of terror that were beginning to unfold around the world.

The French sensed that their country was gaining daily in status. Economic prosperity was growing, as was the country's reputation as an international power of consequence. Even the newspapers had grown smug, happy to toe the line as laid down by the Élysée Palace. If there was the odd critical voice here and there, it tended to sound muffled and unimportant.

However, there was a completely different atmosphere – that of uncertainty and mounting tension – in the DST headquarters on Rue Sousa. Information, diligently collected in thousands of dossiers, indicated a gathering storm of violence brewing beneath the veneer of tranquillity. The expected outbreak would merely serve to confirm the already-known facts – that Paris had become a centre of activity for international terror.

While a nameless young man sat sipping his coffee in the café of Madame Tarpieux, the head of DST Operations stood by the window of his spacious office, watching the snow-flakes falling on the street below. And just like the young man in the café, the Head of DST Operations kept glancing at his watch.

It was precisely 9.25 a.m.

The Head of Operations was waiting impatiently for the return of one of his best officers, Harens, from a rendezvous with a senior representative of Israel's espionage services. The Head of Operations attached considerable importance to that meeting.

Up to that moment, by way of threats, appeasement and entreaties, the DST had managed to avoid an outbreak of politically-inspired bloodshed in the city, and to steer clear of the main arena of international terror. Violence, however, was clearly expected in other centres, and what had made the department uneasy was the growing knowledge that the seeds of this terror had been planted in the French capital.

The Head of Operations could already list the countries directly involved – Britain, because of IRA representatives in Paris; Spain, whose Basque terrorists used France freely; West Germany, where there was an acute awareness of the help in money and arms flowing from Paris to the Baader-Meinhof group; Japan's Red Army, Turkey and, of course, Israel – but it was from the French capital that operations against the Jewish State were being masterminded.

Because of his knowledge of their intelligence service, the Head of Operations secretly admired the Israelis – a sympathy which was widespread throughout the French armed forces. The Israelis were, after all, fighting a bitter battle against Terror International, even though they knew it to be backed by immense political forces – forces which were also alien to the French democratic way of life.

But the Head of Operations knew his duty. His job was to prevent street battles between the adversaries in Paris. Harens's meeting that morning was designed to prolong the truce forced on the Israelis by the French government – though it was generally suspected that the days of peace would soon be over.

Standing at the window, watching the snow fall, the Head of Operations thought back to the previous Minister of the Interior, Raymond Marcellan, who had clearly been possessed of unusual insight when he set up the DST and defined its duties.

'So far,' Marcellan had said, 'France has been lucky to escape the terrorist strikes, but we have information that indicates tomorrow will be different. As I assess it, the terror organizations are backed by powerful countries which I shall not name at this stage. Accordingly, I would define the role of the new department as a continuing action against Leftists who are operating here under the inspiration of an international conspiracy.'

An international conspiracy . . .

That, thought the Head of Operations, was exactly what

it had turned out to be. And the identities of the powers that were trying to undermine the foundations of the Western world and throw it into dangerous anarchy were now crystal clear. It was now almost possible to trace the threads of this development: one way to the Soviet Union and Cuba with their Marxist imprint; the other to Red China and her satellites, chained to Maoism.

Again, he glanced at the wall clock.

Harens was taking too long. The Head of Operations now wondered, and worried, about the delay.

The meeting with the Israeli representative was of particular importance, for it was taking place at the express request of the Minister of the Interior. An accumulation of data had pointed to the fact that Israel was resolved to strike at the terrorists no matter where they might be – and that, clearly, meant dragging in France.

Until recently the Israelis had reluctantly kept their promise to make Paris a neutral zone; but the last massacres – at Lod Airport and at the Munich Games – had caused a drastic change in the attitude of the small, beleagured nation. Israel was now ready to strike back – right here in France – and it seemed to the Minister that this action would lead to a prolonged and brutal conflict with unpredictable political results, both internally and abroad.

It was now close to ten o'clock. Harens still hadn't arrived. The Head of Operations cursed aloud. Only then did he notice that the snow was no longer falling, that in the street below the white, settled flakes were turning into a dirty grey sludge under the tyres of the passing cars . . .

The young man in Madame Tarpieux's café had not moved. He was still waiting. He had to be absolutely certain that the strike would get the man, but not the girl. He remembered the exact distance between the enormous double bed and the table by the window. He wanted the girl to be in the bed. He wanted the man to be at the window. Obviously they were now making love. He wanted them drowsy . . .

Lazily, the young man studied the old grey buildings of the street. He was fond of the Latin Quarter. He thought of it as one of the most colourful in the capitals of the world. Most of the foreigners in Paris, whether students, artists or just plain anarchists, preferred to live in this district. For here a man could fade into the background, become inconspicuous ...

'Monsieur, another coffee?'

He looked up at the girl. He seemed shy and embarrassed. He was obviously a sensitive young man, and she thought him attractive.

'No, thank you,' he said. 'But may I pay you now?'

He paid the girl and she left. He looked across the street. Over there, in a second-storey apartment, its shutters tightly closed, terrorist was making love to his mistress. The young man hoped that soon they would be dozing ...

During his stay in Paris, the young 'executioner' had made a thorough study of the time-table maintained by Hamshari. With the precision of a true professional he had reconstructed the nature of Hamshari's love trysts with the young wife of Pierre Domar, a minor clerk in the Ministry of Posts who lived near the Place de l'Opera.

Every morning at 7.25 Pierre Domar left his modest apartment to go to the nearby post office where he sold stamps. By 8.30 his wife, Jeanette, would also have departed, invariably carrying an innocent shopping bag. She would then stroll to the nearest corner where, at precisely 8.35, a yellow Peugeot always picked her up.

The rest was mundane. A little sordid even. A simple story of infidelity and illicit sex.

The only thing unusual about it was the time of day.

The young man in the café now inhaled and buttoned up his coat. He picked up his briefcase and walked to the back of the café. At the entrance to the service basement he turned and skipped lightly down the stairs.

The basement was neglected. The walls were covered with graffiti. He turned to the public telephone installed next to the toilet cubicles, but saw an elderly workman standing there. The workman was concentrating hard on a prolonged call of nature. He seemed to be taking ages. The young man busied himself with searching through an address book, and finally the workman walked away. He stood at the bottom of the stairs. The young man picked up the phone. There was a minute or two before dialling. He stood there patiently, holding the telephone, waiting while the workman struggled with the fly buttons that were obstinately refusing to close . . .

The telephone rang. Hamshari regained his alertness. Jeanette opened her eyes to see him get off the bed in one easy, well-muscled movement. Hamshari was naked. He walked across the room. He went to the table by the window and he picked up the telephone.

It was the last conscious movement he would ever make.

The air was rent by a fearful explosion. Jeanette screamed. The heavy table was blown apart, and windows and shutters were torn from their frames. Jeanette continued to scream. Cold air rushed into the room: there was a hole in the wall and the kitchen was also in ruins. Jeanette was deafened. She didn't know where she was. She realized that she was lying on the floor and the bed had collapsed. A pall of grey smoke drifted slowly across the room from the spot where Hamshari had been standing. Hamshari had disappeared.

Then she saw him. She was stunned and she blinked. He was lying unconscious on the floor and he was several feet away. Jeanette crawled towards him. She was down on all fours. She was naked and her hair was dishevelled and she felt terrified.

Hamshari was motionless. His belly had been ripped open. She couldn't see his sex organs, only blood and a white flash of bone. Jeanette jerked back and screamed.

That was how Hamshari's two bodyguards, bursting into the apartment, found her. She was kneeling on the floor, her head was thrown back, and she was screaming in half-demented hysteria.

The 'Hunter' had done his job.

At noon, Harens walked into the Head of Operations' office, carrying an armful of dossiers. One glance at his face was enough to reveal that something had gone seriously wrong.

Sinking gratefully into an armchair, Harens first related how he had picked up a Latin Quarter communique on a slaying. But before going into details, he briefly reviewed his meeting with the Israeli espionage representative.

It had taken place in a quiet café in St. Germain de Prés. This was the first time, Harens reported, that the man had refused to give a clear-cut answer. Harens had picked up the impression that the man no longer had authority to agree on any kind of joint policy with the French authorities.

'We parted empty-handed,' Harens said. 'And I heard my answer en route – a very tough and uncompromising Israeli reply.'

Harens then related to the grim-faced Head of Operations how an unknown agent had succeeded in penetrating Hamshari's apartment despite its protective ring of bodyguards. Once in, he had installed a 200 gram plastic explosive charge under the table that held the telephone. Detonation was designed to go off after the telephone rang and as Hamshari completed the circuit by lifting the receiver off its cradle. The explosion had been fatal. Hamshari was mortally wounded, and it was anticipated that he could only live a few more weeks.

Mahmud Hamshari was a name known to the Head of Operations.

From the considerable accumulation of data on his exploits, the Head of Operations knew that the Arab was a top man in the operational side of a terror network in the French capital. It had been established there on the instructions of Dr. George Habash, leader of the Popular Front for the Liberation of Palestine.

'It was a well executed strike,' Harens continued. 'The unknown slipped through Hamshari's highly organized personal security system. He didn't make the slightest mistake and we have no leads. He has to be a professional of rare talent. To the best of my knowledge none of the rival Arab factions have a man capable of operating this methodically. It was an Israeli strike.'

'Do you suspect anyone?'

'Yes. I've heard of someone. Someone capable of using varied skills based on an agile imagination. He has a Mossad look about him – and this man is clearly one of theirs. The Arab organizations know of his existence and are in a blue funk about him. They call him "The Quiet Israeli". Sometimes they call him "The Hunter".'

The Head of Operations looked surprised. Harens grinned and added:

'That's a compliment, really, because he operates with such confidence, coming and going without being detected. Nothing seems to stand in his way and, as far as we know, he has never once failed in getting his man. He appears from nowhere and vanishes into thin air. And believe me, judging from what I've just seen, the man is effective.'

The Head of Operations sighed. 'Well,' he said, after giving some thought to the matter, 'if the Israelis have put their best man into Paris – which appears to be what you are suggesting – then the truce is over.'

'Precisely,' Harens said. 'We're no longer neutral observers. As from now, we are in it, whether we like it or not.'

'Any idea who the next victim might be?'

'Yes.' Harens picked up the dossiers from Archives. 'Here is all the material on Hamshari. Among other items, we have reason to believe that he wasn't the top man. Somebody else has that job. The Israelis will go for him.'

'Who is he?'

'The Israelis call him "Bluebeard" or "The Man with the Thousand Faces". They know that he has an extraordinary influence over women and uses them to serve his purposes. According to our information, he's an Algerian – Muhamad Boudia. And if my suspicions are correct, he will be the next Israeli target.'

'The same executioner?'

'Probably.'

'All right,' said the Head of Operations. 'Find out if this Boudia is really the top man. If he is, warn him. I don't give a damn if they kill him – but not in France.'

Harens left. The Head of Operations watched him go.

Then, with a sigh, he eyed the telephone, knowing that he must report these unwelcome developments. The Minister would not be pleased. The conversation would not be pleasant. The Head of Operations picked up the telephone. He smiled briefly to himself and took a quick, cautionary look under his desk ...

Mahmud Hamshari died four weeks later.

CHAPTER FIFTEEN

END OF THE GAME ... AND BEGINNING

MICHEL MUKARBAL was the first command member of
the network to learn of Mahmud Hamshari's fate.

The 29-year-old Mukarbal by now had a unique status in
the international web of terror. He was the liaison officer
between the High Command in the Lebanon and its senior
field officer, who operated in France. He was also one of the
few who knew precisely how far the DST lagged behind in
its information on the activities of the organization.

Ever since the conference held to unite the terrorist
groups from different lands, they had given the network a
new name: The Armed Arab Struggle. The reason for this
was simply that some senior men in the rival Fatah group,
repelled by the personality of Yasir Arafat, whom they considered a ridiculous clown with his carefully cultivated un-
shaven jowls, had joined them. A condition of their new
allegiance was that the command should be broadened by
bringing in fresh blood – hence the new title.

The object, however, had remained the same. To strike at
the Jews and Israel at any price – even if it meant an alliance
with the communist devil and its wider aim of destroying
democracy in the West.

Mukarbal had arranged to meet Mahmud Hamshari in
his apartment at 1.45, and had flown from Beirut for the
rendezvous. When he arrived for this meeting, the PFLP
man needed only a quick glance to understand that something was seriously amiss. The police cars outside the building told their own story. Mukarbal would now have to

deliver the large sums of money he had brought from Beirut directly to Muhamad Boudia.

From the crowds gathered on the pavement opposite the devastated apartment, Mukarbal gathered as much information as he could about the assassination. With growing dismay he pieced the story together, and surmised that if the Israelis had broken Hamshari's cover, then they would shortly be on the track of Muhamad Boudia.

After edging as close as he dared to the police cordon, to try and hear what they were saying, Mukarbal ambled casually away. It was 12.30. He knew where he would find Boudia. The commander held court every day at this hour at the well-known *de la Ost Parisienne* theatre.

Among theatre circles Muhamad Boudia had by now an enviable reputation as a talented actor and highly imaginative stage director. The critics noted in particular his vitality and ability to identify totally with the characters he played. His spectrum was wide. He was capable of appearing one night as a youth of twenty, the next as a senile old man. As a director, he displayed a keen sensitivity for the material he handled, his favourites being the modern classic playwrights: Dürrenmatt, Ionesco and Samuel Beckett.

None of his colleagues in the theatre could possibly have guessed that Boudia, with his immense personal charm and commitment to culture, was leading many different lives.

To certain circles in Algeria, Boudia was a national hero because of his stalwart opposition to Boumedienne and what he represented. To the high command of international terror he was their ace operative. And to the Israeli who would shortly uncover his true role, he was a despicable, cold-blooded murderer of innocent civilians.

However, on the surface, at least in that early winter of 1972, Boudia was a permanent member of the management of the *de la Ost Parisienne* theatre, where he was proving himself to be a master of the arts, with undisputed prestige and authority.

At noon on the day of Hamshari's assassination, Boudia was busy with his public career. He was helping a young director to stage Beckett's *Endgame*, a play which Boudia considered to be a sign post in the history of the modern theatre. During the morning, he had worked with the electrician at placing the spotlights – Boudia was most meticulous about the smallest detail – and at 12.30 he decided to take a break.

He strolled over to a nearby restaurant, which was where Harens found him, over a bowl of highly spiced onion soup.

The police officer had spotted Boudia through a window. Though he knew him to be in his late thirties, Harens would have been unable to guess his age with certainty. It was this asset which enabled the Algerian to play the parts of youngsters so convincingly. His features were rather broad, as if slightly swollen; and he was of average height with broad shoulders, dominating an ungainly, but flexible and powerful body.

In a measured pace, Harens made his way carefully between the tables to the corner where Boudia was sitting. The Algerian, even though he had spotted the officer as he came into the restaurant, merely raised his head when the inspector stood facing him. They had met fleetingly before and had exchanged a few sentences, but no more than that.

'May I join you?' the inspector asked politely.

'Please,' Boudia said. 'Make yourself at home.'

Boudia's French was as flawless as his Spanish, Italian, Arabic and English. The two men exchanged a few pleasantries, then Harens lowered his voice and got down to business.

'One of your friends was badly hurt today,' he said.

Boudia looked puzzled. 'My friends?' he said.

'Yes,' Harens said. 'A man by the name of Hamshari. Mahmud Hamshari.'

The expression on Boudia's face did not change. He was quizzical, polite.

'Yes,' he said. 'I know him vaguely. But no more than that. What has this got to do with me?'

'It was an attempt on his life,' Harens said. 'And we think that you're next in line ...'

Boudia burst into laughter.

'Monsieur,' he said, 'what can this possibly have to do with me?'

Harens got straight to the point.

'He was a key figure in the terrorist organization that operates from here. And there are fingers pointing to a man called Muhamad Boudia as his direct superior. A certain Boudia who learnt all about terrorism in the old Algerian days.'

'Ridiculous,' the actor said, ignoring the reference to his past and obviously determined not to be perturbed. 'I also hear rumours occasionally; but if I took them seriously I would end up in a lunatic asylum.'

'And I am telling you,' Harens said, 'that the situation is extremely serious. You are the Israelis' next target.'

'This is ridiculous,' Boudia said, speaking calmly.

'I came here to make a suggestion,' Harens said. 'If you are prepared to get out, I will guarantee protection and security as far as the frontiers of France. Beyond that, you are responsible for your own fate. Are you willing to accept my offer?'

Boudia pushed the soup bowl away. His sudden loss of appetite was the only sign of tension – something the inspector was quick to note.

'I know of course who you are and that you do not speak lightly,' Boudia said. 'But I fear that you have been misled. I must remind you that the past is behind me, and today I am a man of the theatre – nothing more.'

Harens knew then that his efforts were in vain. Boudia would continue to deny everything; and indeed, the inspector knew that all he had up to now were suspicions, not definite proof. After a moment's reflection, he stood up.

'All right,' he said. 'If you change your mind, remember, I'm at your service. The offer stands. You can find me at the Rue Sousa. From our point of view, we want to keep Paris clean. No blood. Not one drop . . .'

The Algerian responded with a pained and perplexed smile – continuing with superb ability to act out his role as a misunderstood man – and with a slight bow to Harens, left.

Wanting to collect his thoughts and analyse the situation, Boudia returned to the theatre. As he opened the door, he found an anxious Michel Mukarbal waiting for him. For a few seconds they both stood there, silently staring at each other. Then Mukarbal opened his mouth as if about to speak, but Boudia waved him into silence.

'I know,' he said. 'I know it all. I know about the strike against Hamshari. The police have just told me.'

Mukarbal watched him as he removed his coat and slumped on to the couch. It was some time before Boudia spoke again.

'We must get rid of the Israeli from Brussels,' he said.

Mukarbal knew who he meant. He was referring to Moshe Hanan Yishai, real name Baruch Cohen, a leading operative of the Mossad who was stationed with the Israeli Embassy in Belgium.

Yishai had been an unpleasant thorn in the flesh of the terrorist network, and Boudia now knew that he was the one who had put the finger on Hamshari.

Boudia had received confirmation of Yishai's activities from Nicole, following her inquiries with their contact in Jerusalem after the 'mini-skirt' disaster. Indeed, the Israelis had made a major blunder in sending to Europe one of their men who was so well known – and feared – for his anti-terrorist activities among Arabs on the West Bank of Jordon. His face was recognizable to many people there; and Nicole, Boudia's efficient lady agent, had promptly ascertained that Moshe Hanan Yishai was also Baruch Cohen.

Boudia had already tried once to assassinate Yishai. This time there must be no mistake.

'We must eliminate him,' Boudia said. 'He must go.'

'Yes,' Mukarbal said. 'I agree.'

After a pause, the Algerian, with a weary drop of his shoulders, added:

'Those are the rules of the game: one of ours, one of theirs.'

Boudia was shaken. The mortal wounding of his aide, Hamshari, had hit him hard and given him a foretaste of his own possible fate. He glanced up at Mukarbal and noted that he obviously felt the same.

'Our turn must also come,' Mukarbal said.

'Yes,' Boudia said. 'That is how it is. One day me, one day you. No retreat.' He stared hard at Mukarbal. 'But others will come,' he said. 'They will continue. They will continue and so will the Israelis. It's the end of the game . . . but also the beginning.'

At that moment he didn't realize how prophetic his words were. Within months, some of the players would make their last bow on the stage, would disappear, would be replaced by others. The cruel game would be the same, but the characters would be different – and one of them was destined to shock the world.

A man named Carlos. A man who would be the subject of the greatest manhunt ever. A man who would bluff and confuse the best police investigators and hit-men of the Western world's counter-espionage services. A man who would come to be known as The Phantom, as The Jackal. A man, a young man, named Carlos . . .

CHAPTER SIXTEEN

EXIT BARUCH COHEN

THE danger to Muhamad Boudia was double-pronged. He had to watch out for further assassination attempts from Algeria where Boumedienne's government feared the terrorist leader's efforts at creating an extremist underground movement. Also, it was now evident that the Israeli secret service men were moving in: the violent and unexpected end of Mahmud Hamshari had made that crystal clear.

However, Boudia sensed that the Israelis might not yet be altogether sure of just who their quarry was.

In any event, defensive measures were called for, and it was thinking thus that Boudia with his lively imagination and long experience in the ways of violence produced a startlingly original idea for his own protection.

To implement his plan, Boudia required the services of one unique individual – Carlos – so once again 'Ilitch Ramirez Sanchez' found himself in Paris.

What Boudia had to say when the two friends were reunited was accepted as a glowing compliment by the younger man.

'You, Carlos, are the only one with an imagination like mine,' Boudia said, 'and with other similar traits. The time has now come to make use of these qualities. I want you to stay close by and follow me without any of our men in Paris being aware of your existence. At the right moment I will tell you what I expect of you. Meanwhile, you'll stay in my apartment.'

Carlos's face registered surprise and some confusion, but Boudia went on to explain:

'Nobody knows you are here and nobody ever comes to visit. Not even the neighbours will be aware of your presence here.'

'But . . .'

'There will be no problem, Carlos. You will simply stay here, day and night, without going out.'

'For how long?' Carlos asked.

'I don't know,' Boudia said. 'Maybe a few weeks. Maybe longer.'

'It's going to be boring.'

'There are plenty of books. Read them.'

'And afterwards?'

'After that . . . you can try your hand at psychology. Study me. How's that for an idea? Learn how to live a double life. Learn how to live like me.'

It was a dubious joke and Carlos paid little attention to it. But as the days passed and his strange quarantine began to become oppressive, he did study the Algerian. To his surprise, he found that many facets of this personality he so admired were still unknown to him. Muhamad Boudia had taught himself to become a man of wide horizons and rich culture. He was a fascinating conversationalist and, for the first time since his flight from Algeria many years ago, he was willing to talk about his past. This was, in itself, quite invaluable.

To shake off the tensions of his voluntary captivity, Carlos one day put on a perfect imitation of Boudia training one of his actors. The resemblance was uncanny, and Boudia laughed loud and long.

'Carlos,' he said, 'I am going to put you on the stage. You are as talented an actor as I am!'

'Is there a more interesting stage than ours?' Carlos said. Then, growing more serious, said: 'But tell me, how much longer is this going to last? I'm dying for some fresh air.'

Boudia was sympathetic. It was now mid-January and five weeks since Carlos had first flown in from London. Beyond a doubt, his young friend was yearning for some excitement, missing the company of women, and becoming very bored indeed.

'Not much longer,' Boudia said. 'A few days, perhaps.'

Within the week Boudia told Carlos that he had to leave Paris for a short period. When he returned to France, Carlos would be free to venture out — and to begin his new assignment. So far there had been no hint of just what this job might be; but Carlos was aware of the fact that it held significance for Boudia himself.

At six in the morning, Carlos awoke to find the Algerian sitting in front of a mirror, applying make-up to his face. In a very short time the grey streaks had disappeared and Boudia had a full head of brown hair. A few more quick strokes with the brush and the disguise was complete.

When Muhamad turned around, Carlos was stunned.

'How do I look?' Boudia said.

Carlos couldn't believe it. Boudia was now a stranger. A far younger, different man. And yet oddly familiar . . .

'Magnificent!' Carlos exclaimed. 'But . . . we could be twin brothers!'

The disguised man smiled, but said nothing. He picked up his suitcase and walked to the door.

'Adios, Carlos,' he said.

Baruch Cohen, alias Moshe Haman Yishai, was pleased and excited. He had been promised the identity of the top man of the PFLP's European network within the coming few days. Since spring of 1971 he had been working constantly to get this piece of vital information, and now, late in the January of 1973, he felt like a long-distance runner approaching the finishing line.

The pressure from the Mossad was unrelenting: Find the leaders, whoever, wherever they were. Find them!

Back home in Israel, special teams were in training to eliminate the key figures of the terror organizations that operated in and from Europe — but they couldn't function without the groundwork that had to be supplied by Baruch Cohen and others like him.

The agents involved in information collection could chalk up a long list of achievements, including the leads that had accounted for Mahmud Hamshari. However, they now knew beyond any shadow of doubt that Hamshari was subordinate to someone else – a man as yet unidentified.

Recent developments had made it more difficult for Mossad agents to infiltrate the circles of senior sabotage officers, since the creation of the professionally-trained Terror International had led to tighter security around their activities.

Now there had to be a change of tactics.

Mossad agents in Europe were accordingly instructed to locate the top men urgently, for the purpose of striking 'rapidly and painfully'. It was hoped that the elimination of key personnel would cause the terror groups to crumble from within – and perhaps stop, or at last delay, operations in the nature of Lod Airport and the Munich Games massacres.

The elimination of Khader Kano, a reliable informant, had been a heavy blow. Worse, the Syrian had been removed just as he was on the verge of discovering the true identity of Hamshari's boss, who was also the PFLP's European commander.

The game was now clearly one of life and death. The reward was stark in its simplicity: survival.

Fate at last seemed to be smiling on Baruch Cohen.

A few days after the murder of the Syrian journalist, he succeeded in making contact with a Palestinian who was greedy for money. For hard cash, the Arab promised him the name of the PFLP commander.

But Baruch Cohen didn't know that his cover name of Yishai was now useless and that he was in serious danger.

Thus there was no suspicion of anything amiss when, on 20th January, 1973, his Palestinian informer told him that if he would come to Madrid, it would be possible to point out the man he was so urgently looking for.

Baruch decided to go personally to Spain, and told his informant that he would stay at a hotel in the centre of the city and wait there for word about a meeting. He expected to arrive in the capital on the 22nd of January.

Baruch had no way of knowing that his journey would become a major concern of the DGS – Dirrection General de la Seguridad – at its headquarters in the Puerta del Sol in

Madrid. However, the interest of the Spanish officials would only be aroused when it was already too late to satisfy their curiosity.

On the designated day, Baruch was waiting for detailed information from his Palestinian contact. He spent most of the time loitering in his hotel room, ordering all meals to be sent up to him. It was only after dinner that he allowed himself the luxury of a stroll through the city centre, which was packed with tourists even at that time of year. After a brief exploration of the main streets, he returned to his room.

The time passed slowly. He read newspapers and listened to Spanish music, broadcast hour after hour by Madrid Radio. He made no attempt to contact anyone, not even his closest associates.

At six in the evening of the fifth day, Cohen broke his routine and went down to eat in the hotel restaurant. He was fond of the spicy Spanish food, which reminded him of his favourite Oriental dishes back home. A few minutes after 7.00 p.m., he returned to his lonely vigil. The telephone rang as he entered the room.

'Señor Yishai?' the operator asked.

'Si,' Cohen said. 'Yishai.'

'A call for you, señor.'

Cohen recognized the voice immediately. His Palestinian informer told him that his mark had arrived in Madrid and that he personally was to see him the next day. The Palestinian then suggested that he and Cohen meet at 10.30 in the morning at the Morrison Caféteria in the Unida Jose Antonio, a main street in the city. Cohen agreed.

The Palestinian had phoned from a spacious apartment in a prestige district. After putting down the phone, he turned to a man seated at the other side of the table.

'You heard?' he said. 'Tomorrow!'

'I heard,' the man said. 'Now you know exactly what you have to do? Let's just go over it once again, carefully . . .'

The man giving the orders looked youthful, but his voice was mature and quite harsh. The Palestinian was aware that this was a customer who had better not be crossed or disobeyed.

'I will carry out my orders,' the Palestinian said.

The man nodded. There was no smile on his face. The Palestinian didn't know who the man was – and that was the way Boudia preferred it. Boudia had wanted no one to associate him with the forthcoming event – or with the so-far vague 'PFLP Commander in Europe', now clearly no longer a secret to the French.

This was the second time recently that Boudia had been compelled to carry out an execution personally. It had meant planting a double in his apartment. And it had also meant feeding a steady flow of true information to Yishai in order to gain his confidence. Indeed, the Algerian had spent a good deal of time and effort in the process, but he felt it was worth it.

He might save his own skin, and also reap another bonus: the death of the Israeli agent, Baruch Cohen.

Friday morning in Madrid. 26th January, 1973.

Baruch Cohen finished his breakfast and went to his room to get his coat. On the way out, he had a sudden thought. He went back to the room, removed his gun from an inner pocket, and thrust it deep under the clothes in his suitcase. If, by any remote chance, he was stopped for a spot check, the DGS could arrange many months of time-wasting and detention for possession of a fire-arm. True, he was now playing a dangerous game; but with such valuable information almost within his grasp, he didn't want to take the wrong sort of risk.

A few minutes after ten, Cohen's taxi pulled into the Unida Jose Antonio, also known to the Madrileños as the Gran Via.

Even at this hour of the morning, the street was teeming with hundreds of people – locals and visitors. Amid all the nationalities, Baruch's practised eye picked out the Spanish girls; there was no mistaking their posture and grace. He breathed in the sparkling winter air, so much like Israel's, which shared the same Mediterranean climate.

He was in no hurry. There were still a few minutes before the meeting was due, and he decided to spend them over a cool drink. The caféteria was crowded, mostly with tourists. Finding a vacant table facing the entrance, he took off his coat and lay it down beside him. Then, sipping a glass of orange juice, the Mossad man watched the street outside.

Everything seemed normal. The buildings across the street were a pleasing blend of classic and modern Spain, alternate light and shadow, bright and bold colours. They made him think of Goya's paintings.

At precisely 10.30, Cohen walked out of the caféteria and pushed through the crowds to reach the kerb. Finding a good vantage point, he stood there looking. Suddenly he noticed a beckoning hand. The Palestinian was twenty metres away, next to a news-stand.

As Cohen approached, he extended his own hand in greeting. The response was unexpected. His informant, for no obvious reason, turned on his heels and ran, shoving aside pedestrians and leaving an angry chorus of voices behind him. Cohen went sprinting after him, down the narrow gap in the crowd opened up by the Palestinian's urgent shoving.

Then, just as suddenly as the Palestinian had set off, he stopped dead in his tracks.

Cohen hesitated. His trained instincts flashed a warning. Then the Palestinian moved off again – disappearing through the entrance of a nearby building – and Cohen automatically went after him.

A second man appeared. He appeared in the doorway and he was dark-skinned. He had a gun in his hand.

Cohen plunged a hand into his coat pocket – and cursed. He suddenly remembered that his pistol wasn't there, that he had left it behind in the hotel. He started diving for cover.

Boudia didn't hesitate. He fired twice in quick succession. Both shots found their target and sent Cohen hurtling backwards. Boudia quickly turned around and disappeared.

A woman screamed. She had her hands to her face. She was looking at the man on the ground and her screams shocked the crowd.

Cohen wasn't dead. He was lying on the pavement and there was blood spreading out from his coat. He blinked his

eyes. He saw people milling around him. Finally, in no time
at all, he closed his eyes and lost consciousness.

Baruch Cohen, alias Moshe Hanan Yishai, was mortally
wounded. From time to time, as he lay dying, he mumbled a
name:

'Hamad Majar! Hamad Majar!'

The doctors' efforts to save his life were in vain. Baruch
Cohen died and his body was flown back to Israel for burial
in the rock of Mount Carmel, where a monument would be
erected to his memory.

He had not lived a long life.

The death of Baruch Cohen sparked off a desperate manhunt for Muhamad Boudia. If the Algerian believed that the
slaying of this one operative had made him safe, he was
mistaken. In fact, it had merely increased his vulnerability –
for he had made one vital mistake in Madrid that Friday
morning, a mistake which would strip away his cover.

Meanwhile, he returned to Paris. The time had come to
let Carlos out of the apartment. And from now on, Boudia
and his 'double' were to be inseparable – a man and his
shadow.

The job reserved by Boudia for Carlos was one that this
particular young man could do only because his physical
characteristics were so remarkably similar to Boudia's.

It was a mission that could only have been invented by a
man who came close to genius in the business of subterfuge
and cunning ...

CHAPTER SEVENTEEN

ASSAULT ON DOVE BEACH

THE year of 1972 ended with the Mossad assassination of Mahmud Hamshari. The year of 1973 opened with Boudia's slaying of Baruch Cohen.

It was this killing in the Spanish sunshine that put the Mossad agents on to the real track of Boudia's identity. The Madrid investigators who examined the bullets that had hit Cohen identified them as being of 6.35mm calibre. Since the murder was obviously connected with the clashes between Israel and her enemies, the results of the Spanish inquiries were passed on to the DST in Paris.

Checking through the 'unsolved murders' file at Police headquarters' the French detectives came across the dossier of two Algerians also killed by 6.35mm bullets. The details were sent immediately to the DST for urgent attention. There ballistic experts confirmed beyond doubt that the bullets fired in the French capital were from the same weapon that had been used in Madrid.

The Israel security forces were then given a bonus. Mossad co-operation, in the face of the growing international terror menace, had brought them close to their counterparts in Great Britain, France and West Germany. Information was now being freely exchanged and thus it was that they were handed copies of the DST reports indicating the possibility that Baruch Cohen's killer might be an Algerian living in Paris. Israeli agents were therefore instructed to narrow their search down in the direction of 'an Algerian who is probably studiously avoiding any overt contact with Arab nationalists'.

As winter took hold of Europe, it was decided in Jerusalem to go one step further. Picked army units would now work alongside Mossad operatives – a partnership that was to yield startling results. The spring of 1973 was to be long remembered by the terror organizations as one of their worst periods since the Six Day War.

The night of 1st April, 1973, was cool enough to force out-of-doors strollers to don pullovers and jackets, but a warm breeze drifting in from the sea and over Tel Aviv brought the welcome message that winter was fading away.

For the residents of Israel's largest city, it was a perfectly normal night. The police recorded no exceptional activity beyond the routine bag of petty crime and domestic dramas well known to desk sergeants all the world over.

A few minutes after midnight, however, a phone rang in the Police radio control room. A civilian, identifying himself as a resident of a new housing estate north of the city, reported suspicious movements in an uncompleted seven-storey building in the development.

'What do you mean by suspicious movements?' the sergeant asked.

'I saw a lot of people in the building. Some seemed to be armed.'

This reply galvanized the sergeant into fast action. He cut the call and in one swift movement reached for a microphone linked to Gan Division radio set.

'Gan 5!' he said. 'Gan 5!'

'Gan, this is Gan 5 reporting,' said the voice of the duty patrol officer.

The control room operator briefly repeated the information and identified the site as Lamad District, north of Tel Aviv.

'We're on our way,' said Gan 5.

The call was also picked up by a sergeant in another squad car that was on a routine patrol of the Tel Aviv-Haifa highway, to discourage prostitutes who had recently begun to frequent the main road outside the city limits. The sergeant turned his car towards Lamad and reported to his superior that he was going to the building in question.

Minutes later the first officer, a 28-year-old inspector, was surprised to find the sergeant in heated argument with two men in combat uniforms. The men were clearly not Arab intruders, but so fierce was the dispute that the soldiers were threatening the belligerent sergeant with their Uzi sub-machine-guns.

The officer's appearance quickly brought the war of words to an end.

In fact, the civilian observer had been accurate. There *were* ten armed men on the ground floor of the half-completed building, and another group surrounded the building. One glance was enough to tell the inspector that he was looking at an elite Israel Army unit engaged in some kind of training exercise.

Nevertheless, the matter had to be investigated, so the inspector demanded that the senior army officer be brought to his patrol car. One of the soldiers went off to find the officer, but the second man still kept the two policemen covered and refused to let them come any closer. Eventually a well-built man in his late-thirties materialized out of the darkness. Over his uniform he wore a short flak jacket that hid his badges of rank; but as he drew nearer, the inspector recognized him as a very senior paratroop officer.

'Sir,' he said, extending his hand in greeting.

After a brief exchange of courtesies, the army officer put his arm around the shoulders of the inspector and drew him aside, out of earshot of the other policemen.

'Get your men out of here,' he said. 'And tell them to keep their mouths shut. They weren't here. They saw nothing. Clear?'

'Yes,' the inspector said.

As the tail-lights of the two police cars vanished in the distance, the army officer ordered his men back to the job in hand: that of placing demolition charges against the foundation of the building.

Later, when the tenants of that building eventually took

possession of their apartments, they never for a moment imagined that their new homes in Bourla Street had served as a model for an operation carried out very far away from Tel Aviv . . .

On 6th April, four days after a Tel Aviv police sergeant had nearly come to blows with an Israeli paratroop private, six young men and a woman arrived in Beirut. They had all taken different flights, from London, Paris, Brussels and Rome, arriving in the Lebanon one after the other at various times of the day and night. The last two to pass through customs and passport control were a sturdy youngster and a tall, very attractive girl with Nordic features.

They had not come to enjoy the flesh-pots of the Lebanon – at that time still superficially peaceful and prosperous – but on grim business. Their function was to prepare the ground for a special operation scheduled for the next few days.

All were equipped with perfectly forged passports. All were experienced Israeli secret agents.

Each of them, separately, hired a Mercedes car from local companies at the airport terminal. One after the other, at varying intervals, they arrived at two modest hotels in Beirut's entertainment district: Corniche Ramlat el-Beida. The late-comers, the young couple, arrived with their rented vehicle just as the sun was setting.

It was an agreeable place to stay for a few days. The strip of coast known as 'Dove Beach' lay beneath high cliffs that added a touch of primeval beauty to the waves that thundered on to the wild shore.

Corniche Ramlat el-Beida, with its hundreds of night-clubs, casinos, restaurants, cafés and prostitutes' hang-outs, occupied a long strip above the cliffs. This was an area where one tourist more or less wouldn't attract the slightest attention. Even the Mercedes cars hired by the Israeli agents fitted in with the hundreds of vehicles of the same make owned by the affluent citizens of the Lebanon.

The party behaved like any tourists in a resort town. The first few hours passed without any attempt to establish contact between them. Indeed, they would have found it a little difficult to recognize one another because of the minor alterations made to their appearance before setting off.

At ten on the first evening, they each went out, still separately, to stroll down the wide pavements, soaking in the colourful Oriental sights and sampling the great variety of honeyed confections on sale everywhere. Approaching spring had brought out the crowds.

Beirut's calm was deceptive, for beneath the tranquil surface was a growing tension. The terror organizations had been doing exactly as they pleased, while the rival Christian Falangists were still sharpening their swords behind closed doors. The Lebanese Army stood aside, seemingly oblivious. Groups of terrorists, many in battledress, could be seen everywhere, pursuing their pleasures, often engaging in straightforward gangsterism and crime.

A great many of the cafés had already moved tables out on to the terraces. String and brass instruments supplied background music to Western and Oriental songs. Hundreds of cars moved slowly through the streets, their occupants looking for rare parking spaces. These were the sights and sounds of a city having its last fling before terrorism brought civil war and chaos.

At 10.30, the small group of Mossad agents met in front of a big café, then climbed into two of the rented cars. The young couple took one car and the five men squeezed into the other. Their first task was to check the routes to their target zone and seek out alternative withdrawal roads, should the retreating force encounter ambushes or road blocks.

They all knew Beirut from previous visits.

The direction of travel was northward. The two cars cruised some distance apart. At first they drove along the broad avenue above Dove Beach, under high lamp standards that threw pools of silver on the tarmac. Then they turned into the Rue Verdun and towards Snobera Quarter, a luxury housing development on a rise above the city.

From the Rue Verdun, after passing the Sports Arena and the Zabra and Stalani Refugee camps, the two cars turned into the Rue Ghana, then off the long main thoroughfare

147

into a side street where construction was still in progress.

The cars were now moving slowly. This was the first target. At the centre of the development stood a seven-storey building which was occupied in its entirety by scores of terrorists. As they passed, the people in the cars took a close look at the front of the building, and its entrance in particular, guarded by two armed men.

At the end of the street, the two Mercedes turned into the Rue el-Khartoum. Eighty yards from the corner stood a three-storey apartment block. This was the second target.

One of the cars now continued on its way back to Dove Beach while the other one stopped near the apartment block. To any passers-by, the young couple would appear to be engaged in a lovers' chat, but in reality they were closely studying an unexpected new check-point in front of the building.

This night tour of Beirut was designed as a final check of the information collected over many weeks. The new check-point was an unwelcome additional hazard, and they had to ascertain how many sentries were manning the post.

The young couple studied the building. After a period of time sufficient to their needs, but short enough not to awaken unwelcome interest, they drove back the way they had come, again studying the taller building on the side street. Once past it, the car accelerated and headed for Dove Beach.

Next morning the seven foreigners joined the other tourists for a few hours on the golden sands. They strolled, ostensibly idle, along the narrow strip under the cliffs.

A thorough check confirmed that the landing point had indeed been well chosen.

That night, they again checked the access and retreat routes. Nothing had changed from the previous evening. Early next morning the young woman walked into a local post office and sent a cable to Paris:

'CONSIDERABLE IMPROVEMENT IN THE STATE OF AUNTIE'S HEALTH.'

In another post office at the far end of Beirut, a tourist was also filing a telegram. This one was directed to an automobile parts company head office in Brussels:

'DEAL SIGNED STOP SEND CAR PARTS.'

This exercise was designed to ensure that if anything unexpected happened to one cable, the other would suffice as a signal.

On the night of 8th April, the two messages confirming that all was well were received in Israel. Receipt of the cables set in motion an operation designed to stop activity that also endangered the Lebanon's sovereign status. As the country's President had frankly admitted:

'Lebanon has become the biggest base for the sabotage organizations.'

Israeli intelligence sources were receiving reliable information that study sessions for senior terror group officers were planning bloody massacres similar to those at Lod Airport and the Munich Olympics. Nipping these operations in the bud, before they were even properly organized, was the objective of the strike about to be launched.

None of the terrorists brought to Beirut from all over the world had the slightest inkling of what was about to hit them.

Among the honoured leaders to be welcomed to the terrorist headquarters was Muhamad Boudia.

He arrived in Beirut on 8th April – the same day that the innocuous telegrams were being relayed to Paris and Brussels.

●

As the sun set on 10th April, a typical Eastern Mediterranean spring evening was ushered in. The sun sank early below the horizon. It grew dark quickly and the stars were swallowed up by banks of clouds coming inland from west to east.

At sundown, two missile ships of the Israeli Navy slipped out of Haifa Port and put out to sea. To any casual onlooker, it would have seemed like a routine happening – the Navy's job was to patrol Israeli shores by day and night – but this night was different.

The two ships, making flanking speed, carried, in addition to their own crews, scores of battle-tried Israeli troops. These were carefully chosen men: paratroopers and frogmen. The ships' crews were dressed in their regular fatigues, but their passengers were wearing a strange mixture of civilian clothes and uniform green. While the sailors went about their sea duties, the soldiers sprawled on deck, some of them feeling the queasiness of landlubbers rocking on a fast ship, all of them holding their weapons.

Armed with heavy machine guns, cannon and Gabriel missiles, the two craft ploughed northwards at 24 knots. While they trailed frothy wakes across the suface of the sea, a group of security officers connected with the operation were gathered in the office of Lieutenant-General David Elazar, Chief of Staff of the Israeli Army. Among them were commanders of the units from which men had been chosen, intelligence officers and the heads of the Mossad.

Though hours were to pass before the first reports could arrive with their indication of success or failure, there was a tangible feeling that these men wanted to be together, as if they were all active partners in every stage of the complex operation.

Prime Minister Golda Meir and Defence Minister Moshe Dyan, each in their own homes, were also waiting for the outcome of the most daring blow yet against the terrorist organizations.

Each passing minute increased the tension . . .

Meanwhile, a casual slip almost caused disaster.

The Mossad agents were due to complete their preparations at 11.00 p.m. A few minutes before the appointed hour, the young woman and her companion were sitting in the restaurant of their hotel on Dove Beach. A waiter came over and handed the bill to the young man. He scribbled the number of his room, then began to sign in his native tongue

– Hebrew. The first letter was aleph, like a half moon. Then, under the eye of the waiter, he realized his mistake.

Taking a deep breath, and with scarcely a pause, he changed the offending aleph into a Latin letter and completed the signature with a flourish. Luckily, the incident passed unnoticed. Picking up the bill and tip, the waiter simply thanked the hotel guest and walked away. The young man sighed. His face was ashen-grey.

The girl smiled at him.

'Shall we go?' she asked in English.

'Yes,' he said.

Once inside their Mercedes, the Mossad operative let fly with a curse.

'Stupid!' he exclaimed. 'Stupid!'

'It could happen to anyone,' the girl reassured him, not wanting a jittery colleague on her hands. 'Forget it.'

'It was too bloody stupid,' he replied, furious with himself.

He started the car and drove up the cliff road to a point where the rocks were less slippery and steep. To the girl's relief, he had calmed down by the time they reached their destination . . .

Midnight.

The Israeli ships were already on station, well out to sea, facing Beirut. Members of the crews rapidly and efficiently lowered six rubber Zodiac landing craft into the water, each equipped with a powerful engine.

Six men climbed into each boat. There was little to distinguish officers from men. The only really noticeable difference was in their weapons. The senior men carried silenced Uzi sub-machine guns; their men were armed with Galil rifles, an Israeli improvement on the Kalachnikov. All carried a light web harness of ammunition, grenades and high explosives. In each of the boats, two of the men were naval commandos, of whom one was responsible for the engines and for navigating the fast boats into Dove Beach.

The engines started up and the six black hulks moved off through the water. At first they were abreast in a long line, but as the distance to shore narrowed, they closed in on each other to form an arrow pointing to the beach.

Within minutes the lights of the Lebanese capital gained in intensity. Four hundred yards offshore, the Zodiac engines were shut off and the now silent boats coasted in almost to the point where the waves broke into frothy torrents. They were now 250 yards from the land. A fully-equipped naval commando slipped from each of the boats and swam in to check the beach and make first contact with the Mossad agents on shore.

The six commandos swam abreast in a slightly northerly direction. Their planned landfall was at a point where the cliffs were easily scaleable, beyond the line of night clubs and terraces. Powerful waves helped the swimmers on their way. A few minutes later, they were crawling on to a deserted section of Dove Beach. Bent double, they ran swiftly into the shadows of a low rock on the shore line.

A pair of lovers were ambling along the beach towards them, the woman hanging on to her companion's arm.

One of the commandos gave a low whistle. The couple stopped in their tracks; then the woman strode briskly over to the rock. Her face was covered by a dark scarf, to prevent any of the soldiers identifying her.

'The beach is quiet,' she whispered in Hebrew.

Had any of them been asked at that moment for a description of the scene, the word 'surrealistic' would probably have been used as an answer. They were six highly-trained and well-armed commandos, taking orders from a beautiful young woman against a background of waves breaking on a beach. It didn't seem real.

'What do you think of our date?' one soldier asked another.

'Look for skirts on Dizengoff Street!' came the curt reply. 'We have more pressing things to do in Beirut.'

Having been briefed by the young woman, the commandos turned towards the sea and flashed hooded torches in the direction of the waiting landing-craft. Six Zodiacs promptly moved towards the pinpoints of light, and within minutes the soldiers were wading through foamy water and pulling the rubber boats on to the beach in between low rocks, where they were concealed from casual eyes. Then half a dozen men remained to guard the boats while their comrades joined the first soldiers who were already moving off to their targets.

The thirty men split into six units of five. They were led by the young woman and her companion to the cars parked at intervals along the rocky shore.

The first car, driven by a Mossad agent, moved off at 00.32 hours.

All the drivers knew exactly where they were going. They maintained a one-minute interval between cars to avoid attracting attention. There were no hitches on the way to the side street that linked Ghana and el-Khartoum Streets. By 00.55, all six cars were parked side by side in the parking lot of an unfinished building, and the officer in command, a young and energetic lieutenant-colonel, ordered his men to synchronize their watches.

The operation was to commence at 01.01 hours.

There were two main objectives. One was the seven-storey building standing between two others under construction. This building housed mostly men from the Popular Democratic Front, with a sprinkling from the PFLP, and was the largest single residence for terrorists in the Lebanon. The second was the three-storey house on the Rue el-Khartoum, which also happened to be close to a police station. Three leaders of the PFLP lived here: Ararat's deputy, Muhamad Yussuf el-Najar, the organization's spokesman; a lawyer named Kamal Nasser; and Operations Officer Kamal Adwan, who had achieved fame of a sort in 1971 when he co-commanded the unit that assassinated the Jordanian Prime Minister Wasfi Tal in Cairo.

Eight men had been assigned the task of eliminating the three leaders. The larger force was to demolish the bigger building.

00.58: One of the Mercedes pulled out of the temporary parking lot, carrying nine men, including the Mossad driver, to the second target. The remainder, including the girl, stayed where they were.

01.06: The colonel straightened up and crisply issued an order. A four-man team moved out quickly and confidently to take care of the firing position at the entrance to the building. Another group, employed to give covering fire if required, moved into positions under the guidance of the young woman and her male companion. The demolition squad were ready with their charges. They were to move into the cellar.

01.07: Two members of the team approached the sentries in front of the building. One of them shouted an innocuous question of the Arabs in the emplacement. The two Arabs straightened up – and the battle commenced.

It was short and brutal.

Fingers pressed the triggers of Galil rifles. Two short bursts – and two dead Arabs. Two more Arabs sprang from a nearby Fiat and opened rapid fire on the commandos. Both were hit and fell. Another two came from the rear, firing a pistol and a rifle. The reply was short and effective.

The whole area now erupted into noise and blood.

Terrorists tumbled from their apartments on to the stair-well, firing wildly in every direction. The commandos re-taliated. Men were perking epileptically, clutching at their bodies, rolling down the stairs, lying still. The guns kept firing; grenades exploded; there was flame and smoke and flying metal. The terrorists were cut down, but more kept appearing. They were coming, running, from everywhere. It was brutal and bloody and chaotic. They were firing from the hip: they were shadowy and their guns flashed in the darkness. More grenades exploded. Men screamed and fell. They were writhing on the ground, they were groaning. Sub-machine guns roared. Grenades exploded. There was black smoke and yellow flame and bedlam. The fighting raged on.

Meanwhile, in the midst of this nightmare, the Israeli demolition men had to try and go about their real task of blowing up the building ...

The senior terrorist officers who had been ear-marked for

personal treatment lived on the second floor of their building.

A smooth efficiency marked every move of the eight-man Israeli team. First, they had to cope with four sentries posted at the entrance to the building; this was done quickly and without any problem. They then raced up the stairs, hardly noticing that the whole neighbourhood was now shaking from the thunder of exploding grenades, that tracer bullets were criss-crossing the sky. Six of the men darted to the doors of the three terrorist officers, two men to each apartment. The remaining two men covered the stairs.

By now, the sounds of battle had alerted the officers in the local police station. They promptly raced towards the smaller building, but were stopped short by withering gunfire from the Israeli squad that had remained outside in the street.

On the other side of the battleground, something similar was happening to terrorists who had been alerted at Zabra and Stalani Refugee camps, where they lived. Unable to approach, they fired bursts at random, more to record the fact of their presence than to do any real damage.

In the smaller building, not one of the three terrorist leaders managed to defend himself properly. A short burst of gunfire at the locks, a heavy boot precisely delivered – and the doors were open.

Muhamad Yussuf el-Najar was naked. He had just been copulating with one of his girls. He was shot trying to reach for a Kalachnikov on a nearby table.

Kamal Adwan did manage to fire a few shots at his assailants, but missed. He fell, riddled with bullets, on the carpet of his living-room.

Kamal Nasser was at his desk when the Israelis broke in. He was shot before he could draw his pistol.

The assault team lost no time in vacating the building. They were joined with their comrades outside. The police had wisely retired. Together, the eight men ran towards the bigger building, where the battle had reached a peak of bloody violence.

Shots were now coming from all directions. The tenants of other buildings joined in and sent a hail of gunfire in the direction of the main battle area. In the chaos and darkness, most of those who did find targets got the wrong men – fellow Arab terrorists. Indeed, the Israelis would later be described by an eloquent eye-witness as 'creatures that waltzed around like fire-spewing devils'.

The battle continued. Finally, when the Israeli commander had ascertained that the ground floor was secure and the only occupants were now dead ones, he ordered a cease-fire.

While a doctor in the assault force attended to the wounded – two of whom were to die later – the demolition squad were able to lay their charges by the foundation pillars of the building, in hollow spaces that would increase the effect of the explosion.

While the demolition men were still laying their charges, the Arabs started firing on them from above. The female Mossad operative promptly used her thorough knowledge of the area and the building itself to show the soldiers how best to eliminate the Arabs. She was at the front of the troops as they raced along the balcony and cut down the still-firing Arabs.

This stage of the operation would later be referred to, by numerous eye-witnesses, as 'the beautiful woman assault'. The assault lasted twenty-four minutes and the area was cleared.

Finally, the demolition men moved out, firing at the upper floors as they ran. An order was then given to hold fast until the charges had exploded.

The charges went off. The explosion was tremendous. It beat at their eardrums, scorched the air, then slowly subsided into an eerie silence.

For a few seconds it seemed that the giant edifice was not going to respond to the sudden loss of its foundations. But eventually the unexpected stillness was broken by a reverberating rumble as the building cracked, fell apart and collapsed, burying alive scores of terrorists.

The sappers had been so accurate in their work that another building six feet away was virtually undamaged.

The time had come to withdraw.

Six Mercedes drove out, one after the other, while the occupants continued to fire through the windows to discourage any ideas of pursuit.

In one of the cars the doctor was busily tending the wounded . . .

Long after the fleet of cars had disappeared, there were still blood-curdling screams being raised to the heavens in the smoke-filled, body-strewn battle area.

'Yahud! Yahud! Yahud!'

The cries had started at the height of the fighting. Now they were echoing over the refugee camps, where hundreds of armed men were milling around, bellowing with fright and rage, yet making no attempt to reach the actual battlefield.

'Yahud! Yahud!'

The word alone had a paralysing effect. The total surprise of the attack had thrown the whole area into bewildered panic. Shots were being fired in every direction long after the invading force had departed. For miles around, Arabs were shooting at each other, convinced that they were shooting at the Jews. Nobody thought of alerting forces to block the roads. Nobody considered that this was the moment to seal off all exits from Beirut, as well as main roads within the city. Nothing was organized.

'Yahud! Yahud!'

The cries went on for a long time. They were desperate and automatic. They were accompanied by the barking of packs of dogs in the refugee camps . . .

Out at sea, the Israeli missile ships had kept moving at cruising speed. After dropping the attacking force, they had turned seaward with the intention of creating an impression of routine patrol.

There was growing concern among the sailors. They knew that the battle must now be at its peak and that each passing

minute increased the danger. The raiders were to make contact when they returned to the beach. It was this call that
the sailors were anxiously awaiting.

At 02.00, the sister ships were near the point of rendezvous
with the Zodiacs. So were two 205 helicopters of the Israeli
Air Force. The pilots were tense and expectant, waiting for
the closing stages of the operation. Meanwhile, they hovered
low over the gently rolling Israeli ships.

Contact was made a few minutes later.

'We have wounded. Send helicopter . . .'

The helicopters altered course for Dove Beach. Some way
out, they spotted the flashlights beckoning them to the raiding force.

Withdrawal of the raiders proceeded as planned, with no
unforeseen difficulties. Not a single unit of the Lebanese
Army, police or even a terrorist group was in evidence along
their escape route. No one attempted to ambush or otherwise
stop the strange convoy of Mercedes cars. In the annals of
war, the choice of transport was clearly the most unorthodox
ever used by an attacking force of commandos . . .

Within a matter of minutes they were back where they
had started, close to the Dove Beach night clubs. The
soldiers darted from the cars, some carrying the bodies of
their dead and wounded. Out of the darkness loomed the
shapes of the naval commandos who had stayed to guard the
boats.

Moments after the first radio contact with the mother
ships, the roar of helicopters could be heard as they landed a
few score yards from the assembly point. The dead and
wounded were quickly placed on board the first helicopter.
While it was taking off, the six men and one woman from the
Mossad clambered on to the second one.

Now the paratroopers and commandos pushed their flat-
bottomed boats out into the cold water. The helicopters vanished into the dark sky. The men hauled themselves into
their craft. The naval commanders then started the powerful
engines and guided the boats out over the breakers to the
open sea.

A cool night breeze fanned the faces of the sweating,

exhausted men. It would be a short, fast ride out to the waiting missile ships, then home . . .

At dawn, various important personalities connected with the terrorist organizations poured into the area of the battle zone to see for themselves what had happened. Among them were Yasir Arafat and Nayef Hawatmeh. (A few days later it would become clear that Yasir Arafat had been aware of the nature of the battle. He was told about it while at a meeting with the President of the Lebanon to decide the scope of government aid for his organization. Neither he nor the President went to see what was happening.) Minutes later, they were joined by Suleiman Franjieh, President of the Lebanon. They picked their way carefully through the wreckage, silently observing the arduous attempts to extricate bodies of dead terrorists from the rubble.

Not a single civilian living in the area had been hurt – only terrorists.

The raid had been, from the Israeli point of view, a dazzling success. In fact it turned out to be one of the most devastating blows that Israel was ever to strike at the terrorist organizations.

And if it was of any comfort to Baruch Cohen's family, it was also a bloody and resounding revenge . . .

Muhamad Boudia had arrived at the building shortly after the raiding force left it, and he promptly went to work helping to rescue the wounded. He had spent the late hours of the evening in a dance club, listening to well-known singers, and it was two in the morning before he returned to his apartment. Immediately upon seeing the destruction, he realized just how lucky he had been.

However, instead of feeling consoled, he once more succumbed to the poisonous worm of fear that had recently started to chew its way into his normal, level-headed thinking. And he felt that the long arm which had reached into the heart of Beirut to wreak this havoc could eventually close its murderous fingers on him.

Then, as a stretcher was carried past Boudia, he went pale as a ghost.

A street-lamp had cast its baleful glow on the face of the dead person. It was a woman. Boudia ordered the men carrying the stretcher to stop, and he had another look.

Even in death, with blood and grime streaked over her face, Boudia recognized the woman he had grown to love.

Mademoiselle Calèche.

Boudia closed his eyes and let the pain wash through him. He took hold of the stretcher and he stood there and started to tremble. He opened his eyes. He looked down at her dead face. She was white and her face was a mask, smeared with grime, streaked with blood. He gripped the stretcher tighter, trying to control his trembling. He wanted to weep, but couldn't, so he gave in to the pain. He turned around and walked away.

Vengeance!

He thought about it. It burned through him, it consumed him. He wandered blindly through the darkness, past the wounded, past the dead, and his hatred for the Israelis increased, drove him close to madness.

Vengeance!

He leaned against a wall. He looked up at the dark sky. He looked around at the dead and the wounded and he thought of Nicole.

'Blood for blood!' he said aloud to a startled civilian. The civilian stared at him, then hurried on his way. 'Blood for blood!' Boudia repeated to no-one.

He closed his eyes, clenched his fists tight. He was trembling and he just couldn't stop and he knew what he must do.

He, Muhamad Boudia, would now stop at nothing, would now use all his strength and cunning, would not rest until he had exacted a personal vengeance.

He would eliminate the Jews.

CHAPTER EIGHTEEN

SHADOW AND MASTER BECOME ONE

THE DST Head of Operations spent some time pouring over the grey dossier laid on his table by Inspector
Harens.

'Boudia, Muhamad.'

The title was written in a neat and inconspicuous hand on
the thin cover. There were ten precise and closely-typed
pages, and the scores of facts all led to one conclusion: Muhamad Boudia, theatrical director and actor, was head of the
PFLP European network.

'That's it, then,' the Head of Operations sighed, his worst
fears now confirmed.

'Yes,' Harens said.

The two officers went over the documents again. This was
the end result of five months of exhaustive work. Four experienced agents had been on the case, night and day, since
the elimination of Mahmud Hamshari.

'Well,' the Head of Operations said, finally, 'if we know all
this, then so do the Israelis.'

'A lot of the material was supplied by them,' Harens admitted.

'Can we arrest him on these facts?'

Harens shrugged his shoulders.

'I doubt it. This is only information – it isn't proof that
would hold up in court. Let's not forget that we had to refuse
an arrest when the Spanish police asked for it. There's no
incriminating material here. Certainly insufficient for a
criminal charge to stick.'

'So what do you think can be done?'

'We wait. There's nothing else we can do. Not legally anyway.'

'Perhaps the Algerian government or the Israelis will eliminate him . . .'

'We'll just have to wait and see.'

It was a familiar situation. A forced wait while fate made the decisions for them and the DST stood on the sidelines. So long as the French government pursued its policies of appeasing the Arab world, the DST found its hands tied.

Since January 1973 Carlos had found himself employed in a task so bizarre that he could not possibly have foreseen it. When Boudia had first explained what he wanted, Carlos had thought he was joking; but he soon realized just how serious his friend was and how vital the operation would become.

For a long time in the future it was likely that the task would be a passive and depressing one. Carlos would have to remain anonymous and bury his own identity and ambitions. But at least he now understood Boudia's reason for holding him incommunicado in the small, somewhat austere apartment in the Latin Quarter in Paris. Now Boudia wanted to know if Carlos was willing to continue.

'I would like time to think about it,' Carlos said.

'That is something I appreciate,' Boudia said. 'Think about it by all means. But remember; if you agree, I will be placing my life in your hands.'

Carlos left Paris for a few days. He went to Monte Carlo where, in an atmosphere completely devoid of subterfuge and terrorism, he just did whatever took his fancy. Boudia had always been very generous with money, and now Carlos enjoyed the life of the 'beautiful people' in Prince Rainier's pleasure-soaked kingdom. He gambled in the casinos, went water-skiing, and spent many hours in the company of beautiful ladies.

For six days he drove the problem of Muhamad Boudia from his mind; then, as he began to feel the accumulating boredom of pointless pastimes, he retreated to his hotel room and thought more seriously about Boudia's proposition. On the ninth day he returned to Paris, met Boudia, and told him he had decided to take the job.

Boudia smiled gently.

'Carlos,' he said, 'I only hope that one day you also find a man who will be to you the brother you are to me.'

'You are my true friend,' Carlos said, after a moment's embarrassed hesitation.

They shook hands. They would not see each other for some time. They would not meet again while the operation lasted. From this point on, Carlos would know more of the details of Boudia's daily life than any other man.

That very same day, Carlos took possession of keys to a car and a small house half an hour's drive out of Paris. It was a single-storey building near the Bois de Boulogne, surrounded by a high stone wall and ancient oak trees. Access to it was by a side road. The house was equipped with everything that a man like Carlos could possibly need.

Following a sketch map provided by Boudia, Carlos arrived in the early evening as twilight was descending. The Algerian had taken care of everything, from a colour TV and stereo radio and record equipment to telephones thoughtfully provided in every room.

From that evening on, the telephone was going to be Carlos's only contact with Muhamad Boudia. His friend had even installed a scrambler on the main junction box to prevent their conversations being overheard. This meticulous attention to detail again impressed Carlos as being the hallmark of Boudia's mode of operation, as well as reminding him of the importance of the role he had agreed to undertake.

Boudia had also handed over three cheque books, each for accounts in separate branches of different banks. A large sum was at his disposal, and he had been assured that it would be replenished when necessary. All he now had to do was go to work on an operation with which he was thoroughly familiar . . .

Three months passed. One evening, four days after the last telephone contact with Boudia, the phone rang. Carlos was happy to hear the Algerian's voice, but detected a note of unusual tension.

'Stay at home,' Boudia said. 'I'll join you at midnight.'

That was all. Just two brief sentences. Carlos replaced the receiver and sat down facing a window through which he could see the oak trees. He waited impatiently for Boudia's arrival. A few minutes later he heard the hum of a car gliding slowly into the parking space outside. Carlos watched Boudia approach, walking lethargically with bowed shoulders.

The Algerian looked exhausted. As a beam of light fell through the open doorway on to his friend's face, Carlos noticed distinct lines of deep distress. Then the hint of the old smile:

'Hello, Carlos, my friend!'

'I'll make you some coffee,' Carlos said as Boudia dropped heavily into an armchair. 'You look as though you need it.'

When Carlos came back with the coffee, Boudia was sunk in reverie. It was only after a few sips of the steaming brew that he managed to raise his head – and then Carlos saw the dullness in his eyes.

'I came back from Beirut this morning,' Boudia said.

That was it, Carlos thought. His friend had been a witness to the bloody Israeli raid. Carlos had heard the details on the radio and seen the extent of the damage on television.

'It was ugly, Carlos . . .'

Boudia then spent an hour describing the raid in minute detail.

'The Israelis roamed Beirut as though it belonged to them. They might just as well have been strolling through the Bois de Boulogne in broad daylight. And afterwards . . . with my own hands, I helped drag the bodies out from under the wreckage . . . so many bodies . . . boys, youngsters . . . your age! The swine even wiped out top men whom I never believed could be got at.'

Boudia let fly with a string of profanities. This was a new and disturbing side of the Algerian and the change didn't escape the sensitive ears of Carlos. He had never before heard Boudia curse, not even when speaking of his enemies.

'As for our leaders, Yassir Arafat and Nayef Hawatmeh,'

Boudia continued bitterly, 'they were cowardly, rotten, they were miserable swine. They knew it was happening, but they didn't dare come near. Then, next morning – *next morning,* I tell you! – when all possible danger had gone, the priceless pair came to console the bereaved with crocodile tears. Do you understand, Carlos? The big talkers, our leaders! We are the only ones left to do the real work . . .'

Carlos remained silent. There was nothing to say. Then Boudia looked up, his face crumbling into grief, his eyes moist. 'One of the dead was . . .' He hesitated. He looked at Carlos and looked away. He was fraught and he seemed to be trembling. 'Nicole,' he said. 'I saw her body being carried away from the wreckage. I saw her with my own eyes . . .'

He was crouched over in the armchair, his face in his hands. Carlos looked at him, but didn't immediately say anything. True, he was sad at heart – but not because of Nicole: he was saddened by the sight of his old friend, now exhausted, weakening. Nicole was just a woman, no more and no less. He had enjoyed her in bed and he had respected her as an operative, but his feelings for her went no deeper than that. Carlos had used her. He had enjoyed sending her to Boudia's bed. He had always known that his own good looks and youthful virility gave him an edge over Boudia, and that Nicole would always return to him when asked; he was therefore not jealous. Now, he was sad. He was sad because of Boudia. He knew that Boudia had been in love with Nicole and that her death must have shattered him.

'I'm sorry,' he said.

These words were enough. They said everything and nothing. They washed over Boudia as he slumped in the armchair, his face still covered by his hands. Carlos watched him. The Algerian was a bundle of nerves. He was a winner who was suddenly giving the appearance of having become a loser. And in this business, losers were dead men . . .

Carlos's heart went out to his 'elder brother'. He had great love for the Algerian. The Algerian was weakening. He, Carlos, would lend the Algerian some of his strength. He would comfort and protect him.

The shadow was now merging with its master.

CHAPTER NINETEEN

DEATH OF THE MASTER

THE French capital was now in the throes of a suffocating mistral wind. The Parisians kept moving at their usual fast pace, but mopped more and more often at their brows. Tempers flared and even minor irritations became matters of fierce argument under the influence of the enervating and persistent wind.

Most of the crowd in the Latin Quarter were casually-dressed girls and boys rushing to the Faculty of Natural Sciences at the Sorbonne. The term was nearing its end, and no mere mistral could be allowed to interfere with the end-of-year examinations. The Faux St. Bernard was used to its crowds of young people flowing into the faculty building; and for the shopkeepers and cafés along the street, it was all part of a humdrum routine. Their clientele rarely changed: students, housewives, labourers, clerks – the people who lived and worked in the district. Thus no-one paid any particular attention to a studious young man with a thin, thoughtful face who was sitting in a parked Fiat 128.

The young man gave the appearance of being just another student. A discerning passer-by would have noticed a gentle face, broken only by the sharpness of the jaw. The eyes, well hidden behind thick-rimmed spectacles, were now slightly narrowed as he listened to the music on his radio. Yet, for all his attention to the Beethoven symphony being relayed over the air, he never took his eyes off another car, parked sixty yards behind him on the other side of the street, and clearly centred in the telescopic mirror above his head.

It was a grey Renault 16, no different from any other of its kind in Paris, neither old nor new. A nondescript 1971 model. A car almost impossible to approach since it was guarded, night and day, by a succession of men who were relieved at four-hour intervals.

It was Muhamad Boudia's car.

Some weeks had passed since this young man had first arrived in Paris – exhausting weeks of work which now only needed a simple hand-stroke to reach its ultimate purpose – and if all went well, by this evening, 29th June, 1973, the young man would be far away in his homeland on the shores of the Eastern Mediterranean.

The Israeli – for that is what he was – felt tired. Tracking down Muhamad Boudia had been far more difficult than he had expected. He had come to Paris late in May, to work alone as usual, without any contact between himself and his Israeli colleagues.

The Mossad chiefs had called him only when it was established beyond any doubt that Boudia had escaped the 'Dove Beach' operation unscathed. They finally learnt the true identity of the PFLP head three weeks after the murder of Baruch Cohen in Madrid. At first, they had planned to eliminate Boudia in Paris, but when they learned that the Algerian was to be among the officers summoned to Beirut for consultations, the mission was postponed in the hope that he might be hit with the other terrorists in the Lebanon. Their hopes had not been too misguided, for they missed Boudia only by a matter of minutes. However, Boudia did leave Beirut in one piece; a single strike was therefore required.

The young Israeli who had blown up Boudia's deputy, Mahmud Hamshari, was summoned for the job.

He was a 'hunter'. He had all the natural instincts of a man who once on the trail of his prey would not give up. He had never been known to fail. He was, in short, an assassin *par excellence*.

Born in the hills of Galilee in Northern Israel, the young man had grown up in the rugged mountains where he learnt to read the whisperings of animals and plants. From the moment he could co-ordinate his limbs, he became, by

167

instinct and inclination, a hunter. He grew used to the carrying of a gun both by day and by night.

He was always alone. That was the way he preferred it. He went hunting because it satisfied this need and also offered excitement. When hunting, he rarely missed. He could stalk an animal to within feet. He could press a trigger without tensing a muscle. He had an instinct for death.

Growing older, the hunter discovered the world beyond the frontier. At dead of night he crossed the River Jordan and roamed between the Bedouin camps, no-one ever suspecting that he was there. Indeed, this was his world – the shimmering haze of the desert, the white furnace of the sky, the bright stars in the cold dark of the wilderness night – he merged with the landscape, blended into it, became as one with it.

He was faceless and nameless.

Eventually he was called up to serve in one of the Israeli Army's most select units. Again, he was alone – sent on missions where his prey this time was his own species, man. These years were highly active. His hands were stained with blood. Then he discovered a passionate interest in learning, and he studied with the fierce determination of a Biblical scholar. The Technion in Haifa became his home; and electronics his passion. He became a genius in all aspects of assassination – bugging telephones, wiring cars, planting explosives – and he was much in demand.

He was called up to serve his homeland once more.

It wasn't long after the Six-Day War. Terrorist organizations had begun to operate against Israeli institutions overseas, and such organizations now became his targets. He possessed courage, cold cunning and specialist technical knowledge – and these qualities, allied to quick-thinking imagination, won him a terrifying reputation, particularly amongst his enemies.

He was known as 'the Hunter'.

He was never addressed by any other title. It never struck anyone to call him anything else. And eventually even the 'Hunter' seemed to have forgotten his real name. He felt like, and existed as, a bird of prey.

Now it was Boudia's turn.

At first the young man tackled the task as if it were any other routine hunt. But he soon realized that the Algerian's strange and inexplicable behaviour demanded treatment different from that given to any other problem he had been presented with.

As always, he started at the beginning. His target's pattern of life had to be learned thoroughly. Mossad agents had been able to supply only scant details about Boudia's personal habits. He was known to spend hours in the theatre, but he would also sometimes vanish, to resurface eventually in various places across the length and breadth of Paris. Recently, he had even taken to frequently changing his sleeping place, sometimes only visiting his own apartment once a week, and never on the same day as the previous call. Nor was he alone when he went there, always ensuring that two or three bodyguards kept him company.

The theatre was ringed by Arabs, all of them lolling in doorways or sitting in cars.

Boudia now seemed terrified of his own shadow. His bodyguards, all drawn from the ranks of trusted PFLP 'gorillas', changed on a four-hour schedule around the clock. Truly, he had the paranoia of a prince, protected on all sides.

Yet this wasn't what troubled the Hunter.

What did trouble him was that the Algerian's behaviour no longer conformed to the picture of his past characteristics. Instead, he was developing all the symptoms of an unstable individual, but one with a definite native cunning: just when the Hunter knew that his target was in a certain place, he would find him popping up at another. Again and again, he got on to Boudia's tail; again and again he managed to lose him. The Hunter knew that he had not been detected; but Boudia appeared to be in different parts of Paris at the same time, and his Renault 16 flitted around like a phantom, first seen here and then there, defying time and geography.

It was a mystery.

However, the Hunter discovered that his mark was

currently favouring two mistresses and spending many hours in their apartments. One lived in the 18th arrondisement, and the other in the Faux St. Bernard, quite close to the Sorbonne.

The Israeli was astonished by the amount of effort and time that Boudia seemingly devoted to the two women. His sexual prowess, as well as his ability to travel fast, was clearly awe-inspiring. The Hunter would track him to one mistress and then, when he was certain that the Algerian was safely in bed, hurry over to the other lady's apartment – where, to his astonishment, he would find Boudia's grey Renault already parked.

It was a mystery. It was baffling.

Another thing that hampered the planning of the strike against the Algerian was the car itself. A guard always stayed right next to it. Then, when the super-cautious Boudia appeared, the guard would be the first to climb into the car and start the engine. Only when the Algerian was positive that the vehicle had not been booby-trapped despite the constant vigilance of the 'gorilla', would he climb into the car and drive off. Even then, he drove with the utmost caution.

After two weeks of this, the Hunter was fed up with chasing the elusive Renault 16. It appeared and vanished as if it had a will of its own. One moment it was clearly standing in the Latin Quarter, the next it was parked in Montparnasse. Then, even if the Hunter raced straight back to St. Germain de Pres, the Renault would have beaten him to it.

Carefully, the Hunter thought over the problem and concluded that the tiresome and infuriating surveillance was fruitless. From now on he would concentrate on one area where Boudia appeared frequently. Tossing up mentally between the 18th arrondisement and the Faux St. Bernard, he opted for the latter because of its heavier traffic, which made inconspicuous surveillance much easier.

Finally, the Hunter decided that there was only one way to deal with Boudia. It had to be his car. This was the one weak link in the chain of protective armour with which he had surrounded himself. And the question that had to be answered was simple enough:

How could he get near enough, undetected, to plant the charge?

On 21st June, the Israeli left Paris. He drove down to Marseilles in an old station-wagon, arriving at the Port city late that evening. A Zim Line freighter was in the harbour. Its chief engineer, a Mossad agent, was expecting him.

Under the supervision of the ship's officer, a team of skilled technicians from the crew laboured throughout the night on the station-wagon. When they finished, something vaguely resembling a pitchfork occupied the space next to the exhaust pipe. It was linked to an auxillary motor that now worked off the car's electrical system. By dawn the Hunter was satisfied. The device and its attachments had been tested again and again. At the bidding of pre-set controls, the pitchfork slid easily out from under the station-wagon and retracted just as easily.

After a light breakfast, the Hunter settled down for a few hours' sleep in the chief engineer's cabin. At noon, refreshed, he began the 780 kilometre drive back to Paris.

One more day was spent on thorough preparations; then he was ready.

Three days later, he returned in his Fiat to the Faux St. Bernard and settled down to wait.

At three in the morning of 30th June, Muhamad Boudia's Renault drove into the street. The Algerian parked outside his mistress' apartment building. As he got out of the car a Peugeot pulled up and disgorged the first night-shift guard. Boudia nodded a greeting, then strode into the building, after carefully looking up and down the pavement.

Waiting a few minutes, the Hunter started up his Fiat and drove away from the Faux St. Bernard.

At 8.30 in the morning a dilapidated station-wagon appeared in the same street, already busy with men and women going about their daily business. The driver, who looked to all intents and purposes like a farmer, searched for a parking

171

space. He finally found a spot between a Peugeot 404 and the grey Renault 16.

The farmer was obviously a yokel and a bad driver. As he reversed his vehicle towards the kerb and then straightened out he almost crushed the front bumpers of the Renault. A young Arab, the relief bodyguard, instantly stepped forward to rebuke him.

'I'm sorry,' the farmer muttered as he opened a side door to reveal a load of vegetable crates. 'I didn't hit it. Don't worry. It's okay.'

The relieved guard turned away. He kept his eyes on the street. He watched the farmer sling a crate of vegetables over his shoulder and wander away to a shop farther along the pavement.

'The stupid peasant,' the guard murmured. 'He even forgot to switch off his engine.'

The guard leaned against the wall by the entrance to the apartment building. He lit a cigarette. Meanwhile, the low pitchfork slid out almost at road level from under the station-wagon into the space on the underside of the Renault. Attached to it was a hunk of plastic explosive and a detonator wired for remote control.

Fixed to the upper section of the charge was a powerful magnet. The pitchfork stopped at a point where the magnet, now activated, made contact with the chasis of the Renault.

By the time the 'farmer' returned, the pitchfork had slid back along its runners and was secure under the station-wagon. The engine was still running. After fastening the side door, the farmer climbed back into his seat and put the vehicle in gear. With the same clumsiness as before, he pulled out into the busy stream of traffic and drove off down the road.

At 9.00 a.m., the Hunter was back in the Faux St. Bernard, again at the wheel of the Fiat. Now clean-shaven and not remotely like a farmer, he cruised some sixty metres beyond the Renault. He found a parking space at the opposite kerb and there he remained. Turning on the radio, he tried to find a station with the classical music he so loved; but not for one moment did he take his eyes from the entrance to Boudia's mistress' apartment building, now clearly in view in his rear mirror.

At 10.00 a.m., the bodyguards changed over. From his vantage point, the Hunter watched the two men make a thorough inspection of the Renault from all sides. They peered through the windows and checked the doors. Then, with a quick handshake, they parted.

At 10.50 a.m., the Algerian appeared. He walked away, leaving the bodyguard to continue watching the car. There was something that had to be arranged in the Faculty of Natural Sciences of the Sorbonne, just along the street.

At 11.20 a.m. the Algerian returned.

He opened the car door and waited for the guard to start up the engine. Everything seemed normal. He thanked the guard, climbed into the car and grasped the steering wheel.

The Hunter moved his fingers lightly on to the waveband control on his radio. He twisted the button as far to the right as it would go. Boudia's car was just beginning to move away from the kerb when there was an earsplitting explosion.

The Renault was blown to pieces.

While parts of the Renault were still flying through the air and thick smoke was billowing in every direction, the Fiat moved smoothly away from the pavement where it had been parked. Driving at a perfectly normal speed in the stream of traffic, the Hunter still had time to hear the shocked screams of some passers-by. In his rearview mirror he caught a glimpse of people rushing out of shops and houses and racing towards the wreckage of the Renault. He drove calmly away.

This time there would be no repeat of the slow death experienced by the Hunter's previous victim, Mahmud Hamshari, who lay for weeks on a hospital bed.

Muhamad Boudia died instantly.

CHAPTER TWENTY

A MYSTERY

As he drove away from the Faux St. Bernard, the Hunter could hear the wailing sirens of police cars and ambulances racing to the spot. This sound did not bother him.

Five blocks away, the Hunter again parked his Fiat. Before getting out, he carefully wiped the steering-wheel, radio controls and door handles. Locking the doors behind him, he casually dropped the keys in a storm drain. Then, sauntering over to a near-by Peugeot 504, he climbed into the driver's seat and disappeared into the passing traffic.

His route took him through the 18th arrondisement, and some unexplained curiosity impelled him to take the street where Boudia's other mistress lived.

Parked before the building was a grey Renault 16 exactly like the one that had just been demolished.

It had to be a coincidence, but the Hunter decided to make another turn past the car. Traffic was heavy and there was no alternative but to drive around the block. The number plates would tell him all he wanted to know, something he had not been able to check the first time past the vehicle.

When he passed the apartment block again, the Renault was gone.

The Hunter shrugged his shoulders and forgot the incident, writing the whole thing off as nothing more than an odd quirk of fate.

PART FOUR:

COMMANDO BOUDIA

CHAPTER TWENTY-ONE

THE SHADOW TAKES OVER

THE newspapers made the most of the sensational story of Muhamad Boudia's assassination. After all, the Algerian was prominent in the Paris theatre world; and the actual deed, blowing him to pieces in a street of the capital in broad daylight before the horrified gaze of passers-by . . .

As the details of Boudia's double life came to light, journalists painted a lurid story of a man who had a foot in two disparate worlds, that of the noble arts and that of the sordid arena of terror and violence. Fresh details from official and semi-official sources kept the story alive for many days.

He was written about as a modern 'Bluebeard' who had manipulated attractive and naïve women. Madame Salerdan, Boudia's 18th arrondisement mistress, even claimed in print that a few days before his death Boudia had said:

'Something might happen to me. I have to vanish.'

A few papers saw a far more important aspect of the assassination. *L'Aurore* stressed: 'As a result of the murder of Muhamad Boudia, there is a serious fear of extensive terrorist action.' And *Figaro* added its own opinion, criticizing the French government for its strange attitude towards terrorists who treated Paris as though they owned it.

The PFLP mourned Boudia's death and described him as: 'One of the greatest commanders. A man of aristocratic soul and vision. A hero in pursuit of peace, who fell on the altar of his faith.'

In all the security departments of the countries involved, Muhamad Boudia's dossier was marked 'Closed', but unknown to them at the time, they were about to open a new, unnamed dossier – on a man without a face, without a permanent address. 'A phantom whose tracks are covered in blood,' as one security service was later to describe him.

Thus, while the PFLP continued to eulogize Muhamad Boudia and swear an angry revenge, the 'phantom whose tracks are covered in blood' was already emerging.

Israel's Mossad first got wind of him in their long interrogation of Kozo Okamoto, the remaining member of the Red Army massacre team at Lod Airport.

The Japanese prisoner talked of a man who had helped him and his friends through all the stages of the operation up to their final trip from Rome to Israel. This man had given his name, possibly false, to Okamoto.
Hector Hippodikon.

The Mossad therefore forwarded a request to Scotland Yard and the DST for any information they might have on one Hector Hippodikon, suspected of co-operation with the Japanese terrorists and the PFLP. The French replied in the negative, but Scotland Yard investigators discovered that the name did appear on the register of departures from Heathrow Airport. The man had left England on 11th May, 1972 and there was no record of his return to the United Kingdom.

Experts in the use of identikits visited the Japanese prisoner in his cell. He was polite and co-operative. He described all that he could remember of Hippodikon's facial characteristics, and soon the police had reconstructed the face of a thirty-year old man: broad features, prominent lips, a full head of hair.

Copies of this identikit picture were sent to London, Paris and the CIA, to be filed for future reference.

Two days after the assassination of Boudia, a sturdily-built young man with a very troubled face arrived at Heathrow Airport. He presented a passport in the name of Adolph Granael from Chile, explaining that he was in London on business for about ten days.

Adolph Granael was the same Ilitch Ramirez Sanchez

who had left England as Carlos Andreas Martinez and who was also known to the Japanese prisoner in Israel as Hector Hippodikon.

With his keys in his hand, he headed straight to the Kensington apartment. A neighbour who noticed his late arrival after his prolonged absence would comment later that Ilitch seemed to have aged since his previous departure.

Indeed, he walked more slowly and his habitual smile was no longer in evidence. Even his voice seemed oddly exhausted.

The neighbours knew that Ilitch had arrived home, but none of them saw him or met him face to face. It seemed as if he wanted either a few days rest or absolute privacy in his apartment.

Certainly he needed to be alone. He needed the chance to regain control of his shattered nerves. He wanted silence in which to analyse the past and draw conclusions about the future. Only occasionally, and always in the late hours of the evening, did he venture out and drive himself to some restaurant for a lonely meal.

Perhaps he was not yet aware of the changes in his own psychological make-up. The murder of his close friend had been a traumatic blow. It had also served to emphasize that blood lust which accompanied his bizarre occupation in life.

However, one thing was certain. The terrorist was a man whose future activities would now be guided by a blind hatred for everything associated in his mind with Israel and the Jews.

As he paced the floor of his spacious living-room, 'Adolph Granael' thought over his next steps. The mists of emotional turbulence in his mind gradually evaporated. A picture was beginning to take shape.

For what he had to do to complete this new scenario, he would have to remain anonymous for a while. But he would also require a good deal of help from the PFLP; therefore he had to make contact with the movement's headquarters in Beirut – and for that he needed a competent liaison man whom he could trust.

One by one, he considered the men he had met during the

past few years. Eventually he decided on one man. Though he doubted this candidate's stamina in tight situations, there was no doubt that he had the high standing in the PFLP that was necessary for him to play the required role.

Carlos's one reservation was based on the man's fervent ambition, and the fact that he was just a shade too slick and smooth. In fact, the sort of man who might do anything to save his own skin.

Dismissing these doubts – since, after all, he only wanted a mere message boy – Carlos sent a cable to Beirut. It was wired on the fifth day after his return to London and it was addressed to Michel Mukarbal. It simply requested that this man, who had been the liaison between the PFLP and Boudia's European network, come to London immediately.

Michel Mukarbal was surprised by the peremptory tone of the cable. Of course he knew Carlos; but Carlos was at an operational level where he was expected to show respect for a man of Mukarbal's more senior rank. Thinking it a good joke, Mukarbal showed the cable to George Habash.

'A sardine behaving like a whale,' Mukarbal said.

Habash took the proferred cable and read it slowly. To Mukarbal's surprise, Habash didn't appear to see anything either insolent or humorous about it. Laying the communication down on his desk, he turned to Mukarbal and said:

'It's not a bad idea. You should meet him. As far as I know, he was the closest of any of us to Boudia, particularly during recent months. He may wish to tell us something important.'

'Can't his Royal Highness come to Beirut?'

Habash looked coldly at the young man.

'Maybe he can,' he said. 'And maybe he can't. Go and see him.'

The abashed liaison man, who had got to the top so quickly because he knew how to bend with the wind, now held his tongue. But he was puzzled, because Habash was normally quite fussy about juniors showing the right kind of respect to the more senior men in the movement.

Habash had ordered him to go. He had no other choice. Thus, two days later, he arrived at London Airport and promptly phoned the flat in Kensington.

'I've arrived,' he said curtly.

He expected a show of deference. He expected Carlos to pick him up. Instead, the answer was terse and to the point.

'I'm waiting for you,' Carlos said.

Ridiculous as it seemed, Mukarbal had to go through with it. He took a cab to the apartment. And, if he had been upset by Carlos's impudence so far, worse was to come.

Initially there seemed nothing for him to complain about. The South American received his visitor with all his customary courtesy. He made him comfortable and offered him food and drink. But this Carlos was somewhat different from the Carlos that Mukarbal remembered in the past. He seemed less humorous. He seemed much more intense. Even his voice had become sharper and more demanding. It was the voice of a man used to being obeyed.

It was only after some minutes of small talk that Carlos led the conversation in the direction he wanted. And now Mukarbal sat open-mouthed, listening in amazement to what his host had to say.

'You must be mad,' Mukarbal said, when Carlos had outlined his plans. 'I can only surmise that you're still in shock over the unfortunate death of Boudia.'

Carlos looked at him with eyes so cold that they suddenly sent a shiver down Mukarbal's spine.

'I did not ask your opinion,' Carlos said. 'And until I do, please keep those kind of remarks to yourself. All I want is for you to repeat what I have just said to George Habash.'

Mukarbal's instinct was to reprimand this man who was so much his junior, but he thought better of it. Besides, running over in his mind the proposals that Carlos had spelt out to him, he came to the conclusion that the man must be mad. Possibly that's what Habash wanted to ascertain. And if it were true, then Carlos would be dangerous to the Popular Front and would therefore have to be eliminated. Mukarbal kept his mouth shut.

'There's room for you here until you go back,' Carlos said, indicating that his conversation had ended.

Mukarbal had no intention of staying with a man who was clearly unhinged. Politely refusing the invitation, he explained that he had some financial affairs to arrange in the City and that he would then be returning immediately to Beirut.

'As you wish,' Carlos said.

He made no attempt to detain Mukarbal. He simply phoned for a cab for his guest and saw him to the door.

'I will be waiting for the answer,' he said.

The tone was low and polite, but the imperious eyes told a different tale. Mukarbal nodded and left, feeling relieved to get out. And it was only in the taxi that he realized just how tense he had been throughout the last part of that strange meeting.

The messenger was pleased to get back to Habash the following evening. With a straight face he detailed Carlos's proposal which was, basically, that he should be made responsible for PFLP plans and operations in Europe. In short, to replace Boudia.

When he had finished explaining, Mukarbal carefully studied Habash's face. He expected either laughter or an outburst of anger.

Nothing of the kind happened.

The PFLP leader registered no emotion and told his liaison officer to continue with his report. Mukarbal did so. There was much more to come. Carlos wanted facilities for the control of the network from a new centre – London – as the attentions of the DST were becoming a nuisance. He also wanted a new unit of men for special operations. It was to be named after the dead Muhamad Boudia. It was to be called the Commando Boudia.

'That's what he said?' Habash asked. 'The Commando Boudia?'

For the first time there was a reaction on Habash's face: a distinct hint of humour. Mukarbal felt encouraged to try his luck.

'A madman,' Mukarbal said. 'Obviously.'

Habash's smile disappeared.

Mukarbal continued with the rest of Carlos's suggestions. And now he suddenly felt unsure of himself, for he could not read his boss' thoughts at all. When he had finished, Habash made no comment whatsoever. He simply dismissed Mukarbal from the room.

A few weeks passed. On 2nd August, 1973, the PFLP High Command convened to discuss new appointments. Michel Mukarbal was one of the leaders at the meeting, which took place in a private villa on the slopes above Beirut.

The first two hours were devoted to internal and local points raised by George Habash. It was not until close to midnight that he opened the discussion on problems in the European network resulting from the death of Muhamad Boudia.

This time Mukarbal was not the only one to be surprised by George Habash. He announced that he had decided to appoint Carlos to a key position in the network. In explanation, he offered Boudia's own view – expressed several times in the months before he died – that Carlos was the only man available with the proper talents for the job. It was time to let fresh, younger blood into the top command, Habash added. And Carlos, in his opinion, was the man most suited to the task.

There were no objections.

Not even from Mukarbal, who was soon to be Carlos's trustworthy link with the High Command in the Lebanon.

Mukarbal's first mission in this capacity was to report to Carlos that he had been given the appointment he had requested. Mukarbal also brought with him Habash's agreement to the formation of the special 'Commando Boudia'. Carlos was pleased.

Throughout the conversation, the liaison man showed due deference to Carlos – this young man who had once been his junior and was now his superior – but towards the end he could no longer conceal his resentment.

'How did you do it?' he asked.

'What do you mean?'

'Influence Habash.'

Carlos laughed. 'Learn one thing from me,' he said. 'Never ask about things you shouldn't know.'

Mukarbal asked no more questions, but he could not resist throwing one barb. The PFLP coffers were low at this time, and Mukarbal was one of the men who kept his finger on the purse-strings. Now he attempted to use this power to punish Carlos for his arrogance.

'There's one small matter,' he said casually before leaving. 'We have no money. You'll have to find your own finance for your Commando Boudia.'

The reaction astounded him, for he had grown accustomed to the constant demands for fresh funds made by Carlos in the past. The South American had grown fond of the high life and his expenses in that capacity had been a heavy drain on the PFLP treasure chests.

Now, Carlos simply shrugged his shoulders.

'You can't give me what you don't have,' he said. 'I'll look after it.'

That is what he said. And that is what he did.

CHAPTER TWENTY-TWO

STRINGS AND PREPARATIONS

MUAMAR QADAFFI, the all-powerful ruler of oil-rich Libya, was considered by his fellow Arab kings and presidents to be a fanatical religious maniac. However, he was feared, and even Anwar Sadat, president of Qadaffi's powerful neighbour, Egypt, was careful to use veiled language when he had to condemn Qadaffi.

Qadaffi was known to be looking for a lethal instrument that would do his bidding in the field of political assassinations. In short, he wanted an Arab terror organization under his own wing. If he couldn't have all the Palestinian groups, then one would have to suffice; and already, to this end, he had been pouring funds into their coffers, as he did with other terrorist organizations that came to him with begging bowls.

Even so, there wasn't a single organization prepared to risk an open break with the other Arab countries in exchange for the unquestioned patronage of Muamar Qadaffi, despite the promise of even more gold. The terrorist leaders were careful to avoid commitments to him. They were more than willing to accept his cash – but in return only mouthed platitudes about brotherhood.

It was Qadaffi of whom Carlos was thinking.

Carlos badly needed money for his forthcoming projects and he thought he could get it from Qadaffi. He was quite aware of the inner conflicts of the Arab world, which had left the Libyan virtually isolated. For one thing, there was acute tension between Egypt and Qadaffi. A proposed union between the two countries had collapsed, leaving hatred between them. Qadaffi now lived with the constant fear that the other Arab rulers were plotting to depose him. He was also aware of the growing role of the terrorist movements and of how even conservative Arab countries bowed to them; thus he reasoned that if he could increase his influence over the left-facing terror groups he would inevitably extend his power beyond the borders of his sparsely inhabited desert land. And he believed that in this, the answer to all his problems was money.

Carlos was pinning his hopes on this aspect of Qadaffi's thinking. Now all he needed was a way to reach the austere and fanatical Arab in his isolated stronghold.

He began by organizing his permanent base in London. Since the Sanchez family still considered the Kensington apartment their *pied-a-terre* in the British capital, he would have to find another address. Consequently, he started looking for an area of mixed white and coloured population where his own Oriental or South American features would go unnoticed – and where he could also find assistance amongst the fairer sex.

Indeed, Carlos was now working to the pattern perfected by Boudia in Paris. It would seem that, beyond the similarity of their physical appearance and talents, Carlos had also learned much of the Algerian's doctrines and attitudes during the period they had worked together. Boudia had always claimed that women were the best possible helpers – if you knew how to capture their hearts. Carlos could certainly do this; and in permissive London, with its large population of single women, there were plenty of the right kind available.

In late August 1973 Carlos rented two apartments, one in Bayswater and the other in Apple Court. Both were modest residences. They were chosen as places of refuge should the need arise; but he did take care to alternate between them to establish the fact of his residence. Now he rarely visited the luxurious home in Kensington – and then, only when he felt like a break from the 'slums'. In Bayswater and Apple Court he used the name 'Carlos Andreas Martinez', a South American of Arab origins. To anyone displaying interest, he explained that his family roots were in the Lebanon and Palestine and that they had moved to South America at the turn of the century.

Carlos merged quickly with his new surroundings. The colourful inhabitants were a perfect background for his future activities, and in this hotch-potch of picturesque residents, nobody was going to take much notice of him.

His new neighbours were a cross-section of England's previous Imperial glory. There were Indians, West Indians, Cypriots, Turks, Greeks and Pakistanis. Spaniards and Portuguese mixed with other foreigners from Egypt and a dozen or more South American and Middle East countries.

One day Carlos strayed into a restaurant just north of Hyde Park. His attention was attracted by a quiet pretty waitress in her mid-twenties. She was the kind of girl who would have appealed to Boudia. There was something gentle about her and, as the experienced Carlos saw immediately, she was the type who would do anything for the man she loved.

Carlos sat quietly, watching the girl's every move. She was clearly not English. On this occasion, he merely exchanged smiles with the girl, but when he returned the following day, she recognized him and asked how he was keeping. Carlos replied in Spanish.

The girl was surprised, and a faint blush confirmed that he had been right. She *was* Spanish. And, as it turned out, she lived alone.

Within a week they were friends. Angela had made it clear that she needed someone in her life, but that that someone had to be understanding and sympathetic, not merely an opportunist whose primary aim was to get her into bed. Carlos soon proved he was the right man, polite and restrained, and finally she accepted his invitation to go dancing at a place near her home.

That evening, she confided that she was Basque – a member of a nation fighting for its independence from Spain. Hearing this, Carlos knew that here was a girl who would understand what motivated him – if and when he decided to tell her.

Meanwhile, deprived as he was of the delights of Kensington, the new commander of a terror group not yet in action needed this girl's company. Apparently Señora Sanchez had arrived in London with her other sons, Vladimir and Lenin, but Carlos showed no signs of wanting to meet them. Whatever the reason, while his mother and brothers were in London, Carlos did not move from his lower-class apartments in Bayswater and Apple Court.

To Angela, it seemed that Carlos's affection for her was deepening. Carlos, on the other hand, told her that he was a merchant whose work required him to travel frequently. It would be a convenient excuse for sudden absences.

Meanwhile, he was not neglecting his own plans and preparations. His main efforts were devoted to finding that elusive contact with Libya. A few of the attachés at the Libyan Embassy were willing to help – some of them had already been in contact with the PFLP and had served as a funnel for funds for its activities – but Carlos wanted more than routine connections. He wanted to meet Qadaffi personally.

Ambitious as it may have sounded, this bold request was entirely in keeping with his behaviour since the death of Muhamad Boudia. Now the fervent disciple of his deceased friend, Carlos had every intention of taking his place and continuing his work. His presumptuous demand for an audience with the Libyan President was, therefore, only a part of this emerging pattern.

Carlos was convinced that such a meeting would result in a flow of cash for the special unit he was planning. He believed in his own ability to present Qadaffi with an operational plan that would appeal to the Libyan's fanaticism.

Finally, on 10th September, he contacted Hamid Habib at the Libyan Embassy. This friend of Muamar Qadaffi was ready to spend hours listening to the eloquent Carlos, and the South American was forthcoming with explicit answers to probing questions.

'I have heard of you,' Habib eventually said. 'George Habash recommended that we help you. But I had to be sure by getting to know you myself.'

'Well?'

'Allah will guide our steps,' Habib said. 'Whatever he wills, we shall do.'

Luckily, Allah willed in Carlos's favour. Twelve days later, he was asked to fly to Libya.

This was his first trip abroad since meeting Angela. The night before his departure he arrived at her place carrying a large, locked suitcase. Explaining that it contained valuable property and business documents, he said that he would prefer to entrust them to her until his return. The Basque girl was flattered.

Not too many hours later, Carlos was presenting his plans to the Libyan leader. Qadaffi was impressed. He felt that any man who could even think up such an ambitious project had to be capable of also serving the Libyan leader. The plans, if executed, would require a courage bordering on insanity – a quality which Qadaffi immediately recognized.

Thus, on 1st October, Carlos returned to London with a promise of total financial aid. The Libyan, however, had imposed one condition: there had to be supervision in the person of Hamid Habib, who would act as Carlos's treasurer. Carlos agreed.

Habib proved to be wily. He gave Carlos a sum sufficient for the first stages, but said that more would follow only when he had proof that the plans were really being put into action.

Carlos had every intention of keeping his promises.

The dead-line he gave himself for the scheme that would shock the world was mid-October. However, on 6th October, 1973, a holocaust swept through the Middle East. On that day – the Jewish Day of Atonement – two immense armies, the Syrian and Egyptian forces, attacked Israel.

The Yom Kippur War delayed Carlos's plans – but only for a short time.

Nothing was going to hinder him now.

CHAPTER TWENTY-THREE

LOVE AND VIOLENCE

THE Yom Kippur explosion forced the terror organizations to shelve their plan for an indefinite period of time. War, planned and co-ordinated with Russian assistance, came so suddenly that the Palestinian armed groups as well as the Arab heads of state, other than Syria and Egypt, were taken completely by surprise.

By the very nature of the massive conflict, the Syrian and Egyptian armies stole the terrorist thunder. Dr. Henry Kissinger, playing his favourite role as the angel of peace, used this golden opportunity to try to bring the Arab world within the sphere of American influence.

As the world held its breath, the Arabs ordered the terrorist leaders to remain inactive until the dust over the battlefields could settle. And, since the problem of Israel might now be solved in one bloody blow, the orders from Moscow to the Terror International network were also clear: 'Keep a low profile.'

The Russians were wrong.

When the firing had ceased, one Israeli army stood thirty miles from Damascus. Another had crossed the Suez Canal and now straddled the Suez–Cairo Road.

Like the other terrorists, Carlos, watching the war unfold on his TV set, was forced to restrain his impatience. Meanwhile, he used his time to extend his movements in London and also reorganize the network in Paris. He also found the moment ripe to tighten his links with two other terror groups: the Japanese Red Army and the German Baader-Meinhof underground movements.

Early in November 1973, a young American arrived at Orly Airport, bearing a passport in the name of Glen Everhard. The passenger was wearing a stylish suit and dark glasses, and looked for all the world like the businessman he professed to be.

His first call was at the Cuban Embassy, where an attaché was waiting to give him the key to a Latin Quarter apartment that belonged to a Cuban girl called Nancy. It so happened that she was out of Paris when Carlos, alias Glen Everhard, turned up.

Two important meetings were promptly arranged, both at Nancy's apartment in the Rue Toullier. The first visitor was Yutaka Furoya, operations officer of the Japanese Red Army; the other was Wilfred Baus of Baader-Meinhof.

To both men, Carlos introduced himself as the new boss of the European network and the commander of the Commando Boudia.

Neither man was impressed.

Both reacted with a certain suspicion and the reservation that Carlos was an untried quantity. Boudia had been an excellent organizer, nothing less than an operational genius – they had known and trusted him – but this man who was stepping into his shoes ... true, he had been appointed by George Habash; but, then, Habash was a man who sat in Beirut, remote and safe. Finally, Furoya expressed the caution that the other terror groups were feeling:

'We understand the importance of continuing co-operation,' Furoya said. 'But you must understand that a change of command at this level necessitates approval from the Red Army Command.'

Carlos did understand.

'I appreciate your hesitation,' he said. 'But all you are being asked to do is report this meeting to your people. My plans, you will note, will be bolder than in the past. There will be operations like yours in Japan.'

'You mean the elimination of prominent personalities?'

'Time will reveal all,' Carlos said.

The session with Wilfred Baus ended on the same note of doubt.

Carlos knew full well that it was now up to him to prove himself to the other terror organizations, and to arouse their interest he promised murders more daring than their own assassination efforts in Japan and Germany.

Before he acted, however, there were preliminaries to complete. One was to establish his name with the other organizations – and this was already being achieved. Then he set about reviewing Boudia's inactive network in Paris. He worked many days and nights evaluating each man in the organization. Some he marked for death – a verdict he reserved for men whose loyalty he suspected – and he intended carrying out these sentences personally. Others were accepted into the framework of the new network; and finally, a select few were earmarked for the Commando Boudia.

Four of the most trustworthy and promising men were eventually summoned to the apartment in the Rue Toullier where he gave them the task of revitalizing the network on a completely fresh basis. Carlos, chief of the new Commando, gave precise details of what he wanted each man to do, and they were astonished at his wealth of knowledge about each of the scores of members of the European organization.

It was almost as if Carlos had been actively involved in Boudia's innermost circle right from the onset of the Algerian's operation in Paris.

However, none of the four men knew anything about Carlos's role alongside Boudia in the months before the Algerian's death, nor about the six months of toil as the 'shadow' of the great master.

Nevertheless, these four men, despite their admiration for Carlos's staggering insight into the network, felt there was something terrifying about him. His mouth and face smiled, but his eyes were cold and hard. He was obviously a man who would brook no insubordination or argument. Also, he bore a striking physical resemblance to the dead Boudia. True, he was clearly a young man; but the gestures, the voice, the choice of words, bore an eerie echo of the Algerian. Carlos, however, was much more extreme. He radiated pure hatred.

The four men left the Rue Toullier in the full knowledge

that dramatic days lay ahead of them. The departing terrorists also left as the first nucleus of the Commando Boudia, from which Carlos would demand absolute obedience.

Yet Carlos knew that even these loyal subordinates needed assurance of his personal courage and leadership qualities. He would have to prove that no-one could match him in boldness, initiative and nerve. To do this, and to demonstrate the level of operational performance he would demand from them in future, Carlos planned a single-handed action. This would also serve to demonstrate to the Japanese, Germans and Colonel Qadaffi that he was a man of his word . . .

It was now up to him.

And so 'Glen Everhard' returned to London at the end of November, a very determined and utterly ruthless man.

Angela Otaola was happy to see her friend again. Carlos Andreas Martinez had become an inseparable part of her existence. He was an ardent suitor, though always courteous and considerate – two qualities she valued highly – and this certainly made him very different from the average male on the prowl in Bayswater.

Carlos told her of his success in business, and she listened avidly to his stories of worlds she had never seen. Secretly, she marvelled at her own good luck. Carlos spoke her language, knew how to entertain her, and could remove her instantly, with only a few sentences, from the drabness of her everyday life.

Autumn was merging into winter. Cold winds whipped the trees in the park. And Angela was growing very fond indeed of Carlos Andreas Martinez.

For his part, the commander of the terrorist group welcomed in particular one of Angela's numerous qualities: she didn't bother him with questions. She was satisfied with the fact that he came to her when he was free, and she was careful not to force herself on him when he was obviously busy with his business affairs. In truth, she was flattered that a man of his importance should be interested in her, a mere waitress . . .

Though Angela was unaware of it, Carlos was busily engaged in drawing up contracts with the Angel of Death. To be more precise, he was listing the men whose lives he intended terminating in the near future. In each case there was one simple reason: each victim was connected, one way or another, with the State of Israel.

Prior to Carlos's arrival on the scene, Arab terror had operated on two main levels. First, strikes within Israel's own frontiers; and second, actions against Jewish and non-Jewish organizations that maintained links with Israel. Now Carlos was expanding the death lists to take in a broader spectrum of victims.

This idea had its roots in the Red Army and Baader-Meinhof. From time to time both organizations had 'executed' public men rash enough to criticize them or to demand that drastic action be taken against Left Wing murderers, Marxist or otherwise. These 'executions' had shocked and outraged public opinion in both countries, and instilled fear in the hearts of many elected public servants.

Carlos was now going to extend this policy.

His list included both Jews and non-Jews. The series of murders he was planning was designed to deter many others from any activity on behalf of Israel. But it would also serve the aims of the Terror International as visualized in Moscow at the Patrice Lumumba University. For by creating an air of panic and violence in the West, the whole basis of the democratic way of life would be undermined, thus making it all the easier for the communists to profit.

George Habash approved of the programme. And Muamar Qadaffi was only too eager to finance it.

The candidates for execution, men and women alike, were from all walks of life. Carlos had a short list of ten names for the first stage, but he had not yet chosen his initial victim. Finally he settled on two personalities. One of them was a German. The other was a Jew.

Their names: Axel Springer and Edward Sieff.

He had chosen well. Both were prominent personalities and of a stature that placed them in the centre of public interest.

Edward Sieff was a member of a family with a distinguished place in the annals of Zionism and of Israel. He had grown up in an atmosphere of pride in Judaism and had never attempted to deny his origins. His family were credited with an immense contribution to the welfare of modern Britain and the standard of living of ordinary Britons, alongside a long tradition of helping the Jewish people rebuild their ancient land.

As the head of Marks and Spencer, the world famous chain-stores, and as a leader of the Jewish community in Britain, Sieff had become an important public figure. Also, Carlos was aware that Sieff wielded considerable influence with the Israeli government and contributed to improving diplomatic relations between London and Jerusalem.

Axel Springer was a German who boldly proclaimed his sympathy for Israel. And in turn, the citizens of the small Jewish State respected him as a symbol of the 'true' German culture, as it had existed before the rise of Hitler.

Clearly, Springer was a man of immense integrity, deterred neither by threats nor acts against him. As a newspaperman and publisher he had deliberately erected his publishing house next to the Berlin Wall, as a symbol of his faith in the human will to overcome. He was particularly hated by the left wing terror groups in Germany because of his staunch belief in democracy.

Boldly he had proclaimed: 'I believe that one of Germany's primary tasks is to assist Israel, which to no small extent was established with our horrible co-operation. I take on myself the privilege of saying that there is nothing in the world likely to bring Germany greater international honour than this political road.'

Who was Carlos to strike first? Edward Sieff or Axel Springer?

It had to be a Jew. The first man to stop a bullet from his gun had to be a Jew. His first aim was to shock the world, to stir up unease and fear throughout the West. But it was a Jew who had killed Muhamad Boudia.

There was another consideration. To Carlos, Germany

was a comparatively strange territory in which to operate. He would soon need assistance in that area, and if he succeeded in assassinating Edward Sieff, there was a good chance of increased co-operation with the Baader-Meinhof organization. Indeed, from the example he was about to provide, it was possible that his German comrades could be induced to carry out the Springer job themselves.

Edward Sieff would be the first victim.

In mid-December 1973, Carlos began close surveillance of Edward Sieff. During this period he found it more convenient to operate from his Apple Court apartment, so he told Angela that business was to take him out of London for a while.

Now he had only one interest: his prey.

For the next few days, Carlos adopted a new image: that of solidity, good taste, broad culture and social grace. He dressed expensively, but in the correct, discreet manner. He drove a silver Jaguar. In his role of wealthy man-about-town he had no difficulty in frequenting the haunts where men like Edward Sieff were most likely to be seen.

After ten days of continued surveillance, he decided that the best place to take out Sieff would be at his luxurious home in St. John's Wood, a district that retained the expensive charm and elegance of a bygone era.

Sieff's thirty-room mansion spread over two floors. The residence was hidden modestly behind a high brick wall and shrubbery, above which peeped dignified and mature trees. The house was served by an army of maids, cooks and other domestics, but few of them actually lived in. The only members of the staff permanently resident were the 33-year-old Portuguese butler and his wife; their room was at the back of the house. Sieff's bedroom was on the second floor, facing the street.

Carlos kept a close watch on the household routine. He did so knowing that nobody was paying him any attention since he was sitting in the Jaguar and seemed like a wealthy, well-dressed man. He sat there for hour after hour, taking careful note of the hours when Sieff left home and returned, who came and who went. He committed to memory the faces of the butler and his wife.

Now he only needed to set a precise time for the assassination.

His basic assumption was that Sieff and his wife would have a heavy social programme on New Year's Eve; therefore they were likely to spend the previous hours at home. Carlos would thus strike 24 hours before New Year's Eve.

The best time, he reasoned, would be at seven in the evening. It would be dark then, and the neighbourhood would be relatively quiet. Also, there would be little likelihood of strangers in the house, except, perhaps, dinner guests – and they would not arrive until a later hour. As for his escape route: that would be across the neighbouring gardens to his car, which would be parked near by. He knew precisely, down to seconds, how long his getaway would take.

For the occupants of the Sieff's household, the routine of the evening of 30th December was no different from that of any other evening. Close to seven, Sieff's wife sat in her room while Sieff was in the bathroom, preparing to shave. Manuel, the butler, was drawing the heavy drapes in the living-room on the ground floor. Manuel's wife was in their own quarters.

A broad-shouldered man, wearing a windcheater with upturned fur collar, approached the gate. Turning through it with the confident air of a regular visitor, he made directly for the front door and rang the bell.

Manuel was surprised. Nobody was expected at this hour.

He walked out of the living-room, went to the front door and opened it wide. He recoiled in shock.

Facing him, under the outside lamp, was a young man with a cloth mask over his face and a pistol in his hand.

'Take me to Sieff!' the man said curtly.

The butler was shocked into obedience. Also, he assumed that the armed intruder was bent on robbery; there was no reason to suspect otherwise. Having little choice in the matter, he led the gunman upstairs, towards the bathroom where Sieff was now shaving.

Halfway along the corridor, the lady of the house stepped out of her room. One glance was enough to make her retreat hurriedly. She had caught a glimpse of the terrified butler walking slowly in front of a masked gunman. Her prompt response was to lock her door and phone for the police.

The stranger clearly had nerves of steel. He had spotted Mrs. Sieff, but had not managed to get a shot at her before she closed her door. He obviously knew that her next action would be to call for help; but so confident was he that he could complete his mission and still make his escape before the arrival of the police, that he pressed on with the original plan.

Sieff was surprised to see Manuel in the doorway of the bathroom. The butler rarely came upstairs unless summoned.

A hand suddenly thrust the butler aside and a stranger appeared in the doorway. Sieff saw the pistol. It was silenced. He had no time to react before there was a dull thud, like a cork shooting out of a bottle. A single bullet passed through Sieff's mouth and lodged in his throat. He dropped unconscious to the floor with blood pouring out of his wound.

The gunman immediately turned and ran down the corridor and staircase, out of the front door, and into the darkness beyond.

Police cars were already converging on the house, summoned by the injured man's wife who was now kneeling by her husband. The bullet had come to rest in the jugular vein, and she was sensible enough to turn him over and prevent him choking on his own blood.

Not long after, Sieff lay on the table of an operating theatre in a London hospital. It was a serious injury, but Sieff survived. For a man in his late sixties, he was remarkably healthy.

Meanwhile, Scotland Yard had already started their investigations. The unknown had left by the garden and had got clean away. But one thing was quickly established: the weapon used had been a 9 mm pistol . . .

Carlos had been right. Although Edward Sieff didn't die, the attempted assassination, a rare event in London, received the wide-international headlines he had sought. British reaction in particular was sharp and newspapers noted that the terror organizations had clearly opened a front far removed from the Middle East – a front more dangerous than any in the past, since future developments would now be unpredictable. Indeed, even those not connected with the Arab–Israeli conflict now seemed to be threatened.

Who would be next?

One day after the assassination attempt, the PFLP published a statement accepting responsibility for the shooting and stressing that the assassin was 'one of the most sublime heroes of the struggle to liberate Palestine'. And, for the first time, the statement spoke of the unit responsible as the 'Commando Boudia'.

From one point of view the assassination attempt did not achieve much. Nobody changed their way of life. Edward Sieff, when he eventually recovered, made it clear that he would continue as before; his beliefs had in no way altered. By way of support, Premier Golda Meir sent him a message from Israel:

'The despicable and illogical crime has filled us with horror. Our thoughts are with you.'

Scotland Yard worked energetically at the case. From the reaction of the Arab extremist world, this was clearly a political crime which might snowball into others; thus, the police decided to offer protection to leading Jewish personalities, not realizing that Carlos's list of candidates for execution included prominent non-Jews as well.

In charge of the investigation was Commander Roy Habershon, but he had little to go on. The meagre facts available could lead to any one of thousands of possible candidates.

Meanwhile, Carlos was progressing along his chosen path towards consolidating his status in the eyes of the PFLP High Command and, equally important, making a deep impression on the other groups associated with the Freedom Fighters International.

On 31st December, residents of Kensington could see

Ilitch Ramirez Sanches taking a leisurely morning stroll through his well-known haunts. In fact he was establishing a pattern to be repeated in coming months. As long as his family were in the apartment he would avoid going there; but he made a point of being seen by the neighbours who would connect his presence with that of the family.

At noon the same day, he left England for Beirut, where he met George Habash and reported on his one-man operation. Two days later he flew to Tripoli and collected more funds from the treasurer of his unit. Whilst there, he also took the opportunity to report in precise detail on his use of the money so far received. His thoroughness was typical of his desire to prove he was not using a single penny for himself. Every single item was substantiated by receipts – an unusual phenomenon among terrorists, who were in the habit of padding private accounts in Beirut or Switzerland when given access to the movement's funds.

Carlos received all he asked for from the Libyans, but he still sensed a certain reservation on their part. One operation – and then only a partially successful one – didn't prove too much about his organization's talents and stamina.

By mid-January 1974, he was in Paris again. He had decided that as long as Scotland Yard were stirring up inquiries in London, he might as well check on the reorganization of the network in the rest of Europe, and prepare new plans for forthcoming operations.

Upon his arrival in the French capital, he went immediately to see Raoul St. Rodriguez, an attaché at the Cuban Embassy. (In this inter-nation terror operation, as in so many other subversive activities against the West, the Russians were plucking the fruits of aid to Fidel Castro by using Cuban diplomats as a cover.) Raoul was out, so Carlos decided to spend a little time in his beloved Latin Quarter, at a small restaurant which attracted a South American and Middle Eastern clientèle.

It was here that he first met Nancy, the girl who owned the apartment on Rue Toullier. She was to become an inseparable part of his life.

The introduction was first made about an hour after

Carlos entered the restaurant, when an old friend, also from the Cuban Embassy, came in with a girl in her early twenties. There was nothing particularly outstanding about her appearance, but she smiled pleasantly at Carlos and seemed to be attracted to him.

Here was a woman in a totally different class from Angela Otaola, for Nancy was highly educated and had a wide and cultured background. Carlos was immediately drawn to her. Their conversation sparked into mutual accord and, when it strayed on to the subject of the Paris theatre world, Nancy clearly showed that she was an enthusiastic fan. Obviously they had much in common ...

'You talk almost as if you were a man of the theatre yourself,' Nancy said at one point.

'I had an excellent teacher,' Carlos replied.

The couple were so obviously engrossed in one another that the Cuban felt his presence superfluous. He discreetly withdrew. Four hours passed before Carlos and Nancy finally left the restaurant.

'I live nearby,' Nancy said. 'Would you come for a coffee?'

'Willingly,' Carlos said.

'Rue Toullier,' Nancy said. 'Number nine.'

Carlos smiled boyishly. 'Third floor?' he said. Then, amused by Nancy's look of surprise, he told her who he was.

'I see,' she said. 'The man using my apartment. It was you.'

'Yes,' he said. 'It was me.'

Before the evening was through, Nancy had offered to share her apartment with the fascinating Carlos, since he still had no place to stay in Paris. Carlos amiably accepted.

It was not very long before Nancy had adopted the surname of Sanchez. Indeed, some people were actually convinced that the couple were secretly married.

The apartment at 9 Rue Toullier became Carlos's permanent home and the base of operations in Europe.

Scotland Yard's investigation of the attempted assassination of Edward Sieff faded from the front pages of the London papers. However, the work went on quietly – for the matter was a serious one – and there was also pressure from the Mossad to find out the identity of the would-be killer . . .

In Jerusalem, men experienced in the hunt for terrorists went back to reviewing old files, hoping that some clue had gone undetected . . .

Eventually, the dossier on Hector Hippodikon surfaced. Inside was an identikit picture of the suspect as reconstructed by the Israeli police. It was only a hunch, but . . .

Although the material had already been passed on to Scotland Yard and the DST in Paris, the Mossad decided to send them fresh copies and a reminder indicating the existence of this man as described by the captured Japanese Red Army terrorist at the time of the Lod Airport massacre. The name, obviously, was false.

The fresh material was transferred to Paris and London by special courier, with a memo indicating the importance of the file itself and its possible connection with the present case.

The DST replied promptly – and negatively.

Scotland Yard's answer took longer, but differed from the French response. The English police indicated that they were working actively on this new lead – and would report again.

By now, the Mossad operatives had to admit that they were beaten. The only hope they had was that this newcomer to the terrorist ranks would make a mistake. They were also working on the assumption that a crime of this sort was no one-off operation, and that the terrorist would strike again. All they could do now was sit and wait.

They did not have to wait long.

On 14th January, Michel Mukarbal arrived in Paris, carrying personal instructions for Carlos from George Habash. That same evening, the two men met in Nancy's apartment.

This time Mukarbal did most of the talking.

The assassination attempt in London, he said, was still causing ripples of excitement in the Arab world. George Habash's organization was being greatly admired, for clearly the strike was evidence of the creative imagination that characterized the most noble deeds of Arab valour and terror. Of course, nobody knew the true identity of the assassin. As far as the Arab public was concerned, it was the work of the fearsome Commando Boudia – although, in reality, that unit had not really begun its operations.

Apart from these glowing tributes, Mukarbal had also brought a new plan, with the request that Carlos should offer his opinion. If favourable, then Habash wanted to know if the Commando Boudia would take over the implementation of the idea expressed.

Carlos listened attentively. In practice, the Beirut proposals were a direct continuation of Carlos's own operational conceptions. They involved making strikes at individuals or organizations that used the services of Israeli economic institutions in Europe, with the clear intention of frightening them into severing those ties. Thus Israel would be hurt – economically.

The PFLP had even selected its first target in this new campaign: the City of London branch of the Bank Hapoalim, Israel's 'Workers' Bank'. The plan called for a sudden attack – to injure and kill as many as possible of the bank's customers rather than staff – although, if any of the employees were eliminated in the process, there would be no tears shed in Beirut.

'When?' Carlos asked.

'Choose your own time,' Mukarbal said.

'All right,' Carlos said. 'This month.'

Mukarbal experienced a twinge of revulsion. It seemed to him, then, that Carlos was plainly and simply blood-thirsty. He had never met anyone so ready to slaughter without the slightest sign of conscience. He did not look at Carlos's eyes.

On 16th January, 1974, Carlos returned to London, again with the help of a forged passport. The next few days were spent in casing the bank – when Angela was at work: the nights he devoted to her.

Five days later, he acted.

In the early hours of 21st January, Carlos arrived at Angela's Bayswater apartment only minutes before she was due to leave for the restaurant. He explained his early appearance by saying that he needed some documents from the suitcase he had left in her charge. Since Angela was in a hurry, she left him alone in the apartment.

Carlos opened his valise. It contained pistols, hand grenades and explosives. He withdrew two AM 26 grenades and a silenced Beretta pistol. Before leaving the apartment, he made a few changes in his appearance: a deepening of the hollows beneath the eyes; an added emphasis to the furrows of his forehead. He now looked older and would not be easily recognizable as the man who had spent days in the vicinity of the bank. He picked up the weapons, hid them in his clothing, and went out ...

Noon.

Inside the City Branch of the Bank Hapoalim, there was a sudden explosion. Windows were broken, woodwork was scorched, and tellers' counters were ripped by fragments of metal. A woman screamed. Others lay flat on the floor. When the smoke subsided there was nothing much worse than material damage and one wounded clerk.

Only when police experts arrived was it established that the blast had been caused by a grenade thrown by an unknown assailant.

It was undoubtedly a bold act. Either great courage or desperation was needed to throw a grenade, in the middle of the city of London and in broad daylight, through the main door of a crowded bank.

But then Carlos was bold. He was also desperate. He was desperate to prove his worth to Beirut and Libya and Moscow.

In this, he succeeded.

Again, the reaction was mixed – but certainly there *was* reaction.

There were angry protests from the public and the press – and howls of delight from the Arab world. Once more the PFLP rushed to proclaim its responsibility, noting – as it had after the attempt on Edward Sieff's life – that this was the work of 'the glorious warriors of the Commando Boudia'.

However, this successful operation, designed to prove that

Carlos was without match as a man of action and courage, also aided the search for his identity.

Scotland Yard investigators questioned scores of men and women who had been in the vicinity of the bank about the time of the explosion. Finally, hundreds of seemingly unimportant details again converged to produce a picture of a man broad-shouldered, medium-height and slightly Oriental – almost the same description as that of Edward Sieff's assailant. Moreover, the PFLP announcement from Beirut clearly established a link between both operations. And the attribution of the two terror attacks specifically to the 'Commando Boudia' also convinced Scotland Yard that they had a lead. Finally, by an extraordinary coincidence, a woman passer-by stated that she was convinced she had seen the suspect before. She came up with a name – an American she had met a few months ago – Glen Everhard.

Prompt investigation produced the fact that Glen Everhard had entered and left England a few times in the past year. An urgent request to the CIA and FBI then elicited the information that a student of that name had reported the loss of his passport during a summer visit to England. He was a New Yorker, born 1st August, 1950. A special dispatch from the United States brought a photograph of the genuine Glen Everhard. There was no similarity between this photo and the description of eye-witnesses.

Witnesses of the explosion – as well as the woman who remembered meeting the suspect – were brought to Scotland Yard to assist police artists. A few hours of diligent work produced a picture of a man about thirty with a broad face, thick hair and dark glasses.

It was then that a sharp-eyed detective remembered the identikit copy sent by Mossad of the man known as Hector Hippodikon. Central Registry quickly produced the file, the two reconstructions were laid alongside each other, and all doubts were promptly laid to rest.

It was the same man.

Clearly, the terrorist had used stolen passports in the names of Glen Everhard and Hector Hippodikon, with his own photograph substituted for the originals.

Fresh facts now came to light. Hector Hippodikon had in fact made numerous journeys in and out of London Airport. The dates indicated that he probably spent long periods of time in the British capital.

The police still didn't know his real name, but they knew that he used disguises. They also knew that he was both Glen Everhard and Hector Hippodikon, and that he spent much of his time in London.

The hunt for Carlos was on.

CHAPTER TWENTY-FOUR

A TRADE IN THE HAGUE

FEBRUARY 1974. Scotland Yard, the DST and Mossad had opened a new page in their relationship with each other. The British and French reached the conclusion that the terror business now extended far beyond the limits of the Arab–Israeli conflict.

'Terror International' was now a certainty rather than a vague theory. And the situation was made darker by the knowledge that a major power was backing the murder groups.

Information between the three security services now flowed freely. To strike hard against Terror International they would have to trap a man still unknown, and despite the fact that the British and Israelis had a pretty good idea of what he looked like, their information was still too vague to enable them to spot him the minute he turned up again.

Scotland Yard had to admit that they had reached a stalemate.

March 1974. The French, though not directly involved in the investigation of crimes committed in England, were continuing to accumulate data on a man who might be connected with the PFLP network operating in Paris. Every item added to their 'Monsieur X' dossier was promptly copied and relayed to Scotland Yard and the Mossad.

May 1974. The mystery man had remained inactive through the winter months after the Bank Hapoalim incident. It seemed that he was lying low, waiting for the excitement to die down. Yet the Israelis, unlike their French and British counterparts, were not at all convinced that the man had vanished from the scene. They connected him with sudden spurts of terrorist activity in Japan and West Germany, if not directly, then at least indirectly.

Winter had proved to be a busy season for the champions of violence. In both Japan and West Germany a whole series of extremist, politically-inspired crimes were recorded, ranging from armed robbery of money and weapons to the mailing of explosive envelopes through the post and murder. The Red Army and the Baader-Meinhof made no attempt to conceal their responsibility. Meanwhile, the Israelis were convinced that the unknown would return to his traditional areas of operation as soon as he felt safe.

Their facts and guess-work were filed under 'Adon X'.

Mossad experts continued methodically to analyse the data accumulating on the suspect who, unknown as he was, loomed as a tangible and growing threat. They therefore decided to take an active role in trying to flush him out from his hiding-place.

Yet time was pressing. They were certain he would strike again – and soon. Carefully prepared charts of all known terror groups believed to be partners in Terror International were compared. From these, they pin-pointed the men believed to be couriers and liaison officers who maintained contact across frontiers.

One name that cropped up again and again was Yutaka Furoya, Operations Officer of the Red Army, who seemed to be constantly on the move from Japan to Europe and the Middle East.

Parallel to the counter-terror experts, a team of Orientalists analysed the style and content of PFLP statements claiming responsibility for the recent events in England. Their purpose was to learn from the PFLP attitude what the organization really expected of this mysterious Commando Boudia – believed to be under the command of Adon X – and to try to assess his real importance and aims.

Working separately, at least in the early stages, the two teams reached almost identical conclusions. First, the new unit of terror was still in its organizational phase; but when this period was over a new wave of violence would surely be ushered in. Second, the unknown was still climbing the rungs of command and needed to take short-cut risks to consolidate his own status.

By the end of May 1974, the Mossad had an operations plan of its own. This was aimed at forcing Carlos to take action in accordance with the time-table set by his hunters – and not one suited to his own convenience.

His temporary disappearance, coupled with the growing terrorist activity in other countries, led to the conclusion that he was concentrating on renewing the PFLP's links with other groups. The best way to test this theory was to strike at a leading terrorist personality in Japan or West Germany.

To come to the aid of his comrade, 'X' would be forced into the open to take counter moves – and thus prove to his international brothers his unreserved loyalty and courage. Unless the Israelis were making a major error, he would thus have to act before he was properly prepared. There would then be a practical possibility of identifying him – and, with a bit of luck, eliminating him.

After careful consideration it was decided that Yutaka Furoya was the best bait. He had been extremely active and was an important man in his own Red Army movement.

The plan was to persuade the DST to arrest Furoya.

Past experience had proved that the detention of a prominent terrorist drove the underground movements into a paroxysm of rage. They always reacted predictably by exercising blackmail through a terror strike or kidnapping to get their man released. In the case of Yutaka Furoya, the PFLP would be put to the test of proving its commitment to co-operate. The logical move on their part would thus be to activate the Commando Boudia, led by Adon X.

It was a bold gamble, Mossad thought, but certainly worth a try.

A team of Israeli agents was assigned to close surveillance of the Japanese contact man. The task wasn't easy, and called for close co-operation with the police and security forces in Japan and West Germany. But, difficult as the task was, the web began to be spun around Yutaka Furoya.

Now it only remained to be seen whether the Israeli theory would stand the test of reality.

Carlos spent the winter months in Paris and West Germany, with occasional trips to Zurich, Rome and Vienna. His time was devoted to the careful selection of men from the Commando Boudia, and in strengthening his links with Baader-Meinhof and the Red Army – as had been rightly surmised by Mossad.

While in Paris, Carlos stayed at 9 Rue Toullier.

Nancy was clearly devoted to him and she did not hide her feelings, particularly when in the company of mutual friends. However, the girl had no idea that Carlos was also paying court to a young Venezuelan beauty, Silvia Empara Masmala, who lived at 11 Rue Amelie. Quite apart from the normal delights of a relationship with an attractive woman, Carlos had another purpose: in the cities where he operated, he needed alternative sanctuary in the event of his having to drop out of sight quickly.

Carlos gained Silvia's friendship and trust by a constant display of affection. He did not rush her, and eventually she was ready for the 'slow fire' approach that had also characterized Muhamad Boudia's attitude to the fair sex.

One day he asked Silvia whether he could leave a box of documents at her place. By way of explanation he said that all sorts of doubtful characters visited Nancy's apartment.

If the Cuban girl did not know about Silvia Empara Masmala, this second lady was well aware of Carlos's relationship with Nancy. However, she didn't mind, and she was happy to look after the charming young man's valuable business papers.

The large crate delivered to the Rue Amelie contained the arsenal of Carlos's special commando: AM 26 grenades, carbines, pistols and Czech and Bulgarian-made explosives. Most of the weapons originated behind the Iron Curtain or had been stolen from the US army in Germany and transferred to Carlos by Baader-Meinhof.

Carlos was following a set pattern. His stores of weapons were cached at the homes of his lady friends. This was the approach that had won for Muhamad Boudia the nickname of 'Bluebeard'.

By now the Commando Boudia was an established fact. The men had been picked, trained and tested. They were ready for assignment to future missions. Moreover, the transfer of weapons from the German terrorists showed how smoothly the co-operation between groups from different countries was working. Carlos had spent much time with the Baader-Meinhof during the winter, and had succeeded in 'selling' them the idea of assassinating Axel Springer, the second man on his list. He was quite willing to take an active part in the slaying.

The German terrorists needed little encouragement. They already considered the newspaper tycoon as their sworn enemy. Springer had used every opportunity to criticize his own government for its impotence in dealing with the murder gangs. To him, their very existence was a powerful threat to the democracy established since the end of the Nazi era. Springer also considered that the terrorists were the instruments for Soviet-prompted subversion.

'If the West does not finally awake,' he warned, 'we can expect a new Dark Age.'

With the encouragement of Carlos, whose commando would take part, the West German gang planned their strike against Axel Springer for the summer of 1974.

This project was postponed because of an unexpected, Mossad-inspired blow at Terror International ...

Weeks of intense activity had produced precise details of Yutaka Furoya's itinerary. Furoya suspected nothing, however, as he travelled his regular routes on the instructions of Fusaku Shiganova, head of the Red Army. The Japanese terrorists were impressed by Carlos's actions in London, and Furoya was thus ordered to renew contact with the PFLP. He was to give all assistance needed by the Commando Boudia – a commitment which the Japanese would honour in style.

Early in July 1974, an Israeli agent working in the Lebanon sent a message that Furoya was on his way to Beirut.

From another man that the Mossad had planted at the airport itself came the news that Furoya would move on to Paris from the Lebanon.

The date of the journey was mid-July. The purpose: the planning of a joint operation with the Commando Boudia.

The messenger who was sent to Paris from Mossad headquarters spelt out all this impressive information – sent by the man who had penetrated the PFLP in Beirut. In somewhat exaggerated tones, he explained the possible results if no action was taken by the DST. Furoya, then, had to be arrested.

By now, however, the DST was ready to co-operate right down the line. The increasing terrorist activity on French soil was annoying them intensely and provoking strong criticism of official tardiness.

However, could the Israelis supply more precise details of Yutaka's movements?

They could – and did. Twenty-four hours later, the messenger from Jerusalem announced that the quarry would arrive at Orly Airport on 16th July, 1974.

This information was accurate.

DST agents were waiting at Orly for Furoya. Around noon, they detained a young and indignant Japanese who had just arrived from the Lebanon. At first he offered a passport in a completely different name, protested about being interrogated, and demanded to see the Ambassador. But the DST stood their ground. Furoya was asked to open his luggage. A search brought to light three more forged passports and ten thousand dollars in bills of various denominations. By evening of the same day, experts were prepared to swear in court that the money was also fake.

Yutaka Furoya was transferred to DST headquarters, but his arrest was only announced three weeks later as the French police were hoping to stave off the expected wave of violence which was sure to follow.

However, the Mossad were close to their objective.

Furoya's arrest would force 'Monsieur X' to act differently from the way he had planned. And quite unknown to the Mossad, they had already succeeded in this: indeed, the arrest of the Japanese liaison man had compelled the Terror

International network to put off their assassination plot on Axel Springer. They now had to concentrate on finding a way of rescuing their comrade – and thus proving their loyalty to the Japanese Red Army.

Meanwhile, police and security forces all around Europe were alerted.

The wanted man and his Commando Boudia could be expected to rise to the bait and surface at any moment.

The DST were still working away at interrogating Yutaka Furoya. They tried every method of legal persuasion to get what he knew about the Terror International movement and its plans, but the Japanese was a tough nut to crack. He realized that if he betrayed his comrades, his life would not last much longer. On the other hand, if he remained silent, there was a very good chance that he would be rescued.

'All you can accuse me of is possession of forged passports and money,' he told the French detectives. 'If you bring me to court on these charges, I will accuse you of framing me. I will make it clear that you planted the evidence in my suitcases.'

Repeated attempts to convince him that co-operation was in his best interests only encountered a stoical wall of resistance. All that Furoya could be induced to say was that the DST were framing him.

A fortnight after Furoya's arrest, the Red Army decided to send a man to Europe to prepare the ground for his release. The Japanese terrorists now called on their partners to live up to their claims of co-operation between brothers. Their chief was convinced that the assistance would be forthcoming, and that Commando Boudia would make good its boasts.

Indeed, they had been offered proof of capability only days before when, on 3rd August, 1974, explosive-filled cars were detonated outside the editorial offices of three Paris newspapers. The PFLP published a statement crediting Commando Boudia with the attack and explaining that the papers had taken 'too close a line to supporting Israel'.

Shiganovu chose as liaison man the 31-year-old Tusiyo

Umora. Using a forged passport, the messenger arrived in West Germany and headed for his first meeting, in Munich, with Baader-Meinhof and Carlos – who came specially from Paris.

The terror experts sat down to plan the moves that would achieve the release of Furoya. Umora's chief, however, had insisted that the actual mission be carried out exclusively by members of his Red Army, while Commando Boudia would make all the preparations, falling back on the West Germans if they needed extra help.

Shiganova had one simple aim: to free Furoya. And to do that the terrorists needed a situation which posed a direct threat to a French institution.

What better than a French Embassy?

Now all that remained was to pick the country. There was general agreement that the alertness of internal security in Britain and Germany eliminated both countries. The best choice therefore would be some place so far untouched by any terror organization.

They chose Holland.

This was a target that answered two purposes. First, there would be the release of Furoya. Second, the Dutch would be punished for adopting far too friendly an attitude to Israel.

The next item on the terrorist agenda was the division of labour. Baader-Meinhof accepted all responsibility for housing Umora and the two men who were to be part of his attack squad. They would remain in hiding in Germany until ready to strike.

Carlos would put his men to work studying the Embassy building and planning all the details of how it was to be seized.

There was another, less agreeable message for the Commando Boudia chief. The Japanese were adamant that he had been betrayed by an Arab informer belonging to the PFLP network in Europe.

'The traitor is your business,' Umora harshly told Carlos. 'Deal with it!'

It was a direct challenge to Carlos and he did not duck the issue.

'I'll check your information,' he said. 'If I do find an informer, I'll deal with him personally.'

The Munich meeting lasted from early morning until late at night.

Carlos then returned to Paris and cabled Mukarbal, seeking his personal assistance. This was a calculated move. Carlos was not going to fall into the trap of exposing his identity. To prepare the groundwork for occupation of the French Embassy in the Hague, he would have to go there. But he would want a reliable man to work with – a man from behind whom Carlos could operate without being seen, a puppet answering to the master's strings, but a master whose face was to be hidden from the audience.

There was no one better for this manipulated role than Michel Mukarbal.

The Israelis ordered the 'Hunter' to travel to Europe.

Immediately after the arrest of Yutaka Furoya, the Mossad knew they had a comfortable arena in which to operate. The steps leading to the arrest of the Japanese courier had gone like clockwork. If the other assumptions were correct, 'Adon X' would now resurface – and everything had to be ready for him.

The meagre description in the Mossad files was circulated to all agents in Europe, with orders to drop everything and devote efforts to finding the man answering the descriptions of either 'Hector Hippodikon' or 'Glen Everhard'. Reinforcements were sent direct from Israel to help in this urgent task.

Though he had not done any identification work for some time, as distinct from his role as an executioner, the 'Hunter' willingly accepted what he recognized as a vitally important role. He wasn't asked to kill the terrorist leader – simply to gather up what information he could on PFLP Enemy Number One.

It was a wise decision, since it would be through the Hunter's efforts that the long-awaited breakthrough in identifying the elusive Commando Boudia chief would be achieved.

Meanwhile, Europe was swarming with terrorists and espionage agents. It was a wide area to cover. On the surface, life for ordinary citizens continued as usual; but underneath, all the involved parties were toiling away frantically. While the terrorists went about their preparations for the release of Furoya, the security services in Britain, France and West Germany were buzzing with their own activity. All this made the task of Israeli agents that much easier and less noticeable.

The Mossad forecast was now confirmed.

Terror International was indeed working to secure Furoya's release. However, nobody knew yet where or when the blow would fall . . .

It began on Friday 13th September, 1974, when three heavily armed Japanese, led by Tusiyo Umora, burst into the French Embassy in the Hague. Brandishing pistols and clearly meaning business, they collected ten hostages – eight men and two women – including Le Comte Jacques Chenare, Ambassador to France.

This fast and precise penetration of the building was made possible by Carlos who, with Michel Mukarbal, had spent two weeks making a thorough study of the Embassy.

The ensuing drama was followed by tens of millions in Europe, listening to radios and watching TV screens. Word of the Red Army occupation of the French Embassy spread through the Hague like wildfire, and thousands of its citizens poured into the area.

By the time the curious onlookers arrived, the building was already surrounded by a double cordon of police and soldiers. Negotiations with the terrorists were already under way, with the help of an interpreter from the Japanese Embassy. The prolonged conversations – of which there were scores during the following six days – were by telephone to the instrument installed in the Ambassador's office. Within hours the Dutch were told of the terrorist demands.

What was wanted was the immediate release of their comrade, Yutaka Furoya, from detention in Paris. He was to be brought by plane to Schiphol Airport on the outskirts of

Amsterdam. The plane which brought him was to be placed at the disposal of the three Japanese, to fly them to some unknown destination.

The three also demanded a 'special grant' of three hundred thousand dollars from the French government – to compensate them for the inconvenience the Paris authorities had put them to, as one of the terrorists insolently explained.

Only when these two demands were met would the hostages and the Ambassador be released.

While the negotiations were under way, the Dutch mounted a gigantic operation to seal off the entire district. The country's Prime Minister was doing all in his power to avoid further attacks or bloodshed until the French government gave its response to the demands. He personally was convinced that a refusal would result in the execution of the hostages . . .

If his Commando Boudia was not allowed to take part in the actual attack, thus proving their valour, Carlos was determined to see that the Japanese did not get all the glory. For this reason, he decided to launch his own side show.

Shortly after the PFLP announced that the Hague attack was the joint work of the Commando Boudia and the Red Army of Japan, a bomb was thrown into a drugstore in St. Germain des Prés, in Paris.

It was 15th September – a Sunday – and day three of the siege of the French Embassy in Holland.

The drugstore was packed with men and women of all ages. An unidentified car pulled up at the entrance, and a youth leaped from it and flung an explosive charge through the doorway. While the package was still sailing through the air, the assailant was already diving back into the car, which made a quick getaway. The charge exploded before anyone saw it. Result: two dead and thirty-four injured.

The Paris police did not have to wait long to learn the motive of this apparently senseless act of violence. Within a few hours, the PFLP spokesman in Beirut was again joyfully claiming that the 'heroes of the Commando Boudia' were responsible for the murderous attack. It was an odd admission: many of the customers in the drugstore had been Arabs.

The answer, however, was hinted at publicly and explained privately, by Carlos. The bombing had taken place at that precise hour because the two men who had given the DST the date and time of Furoya's arrival in Paris were meeting then in the drugstore.

Carlos was seeking to prove that he had met his commitment to the Red Army – if not personally, then at least by his representatives – of eliminating the informers who had given away the liaison man.

The Japanese accepted Carlos's word for it. The Mossad, however, knew otherwise.

This was the first time that the Israelis noted Carlos's willingness to lie to his own colleagues in order to further his own ends. He was quite ready to murder innocent people purely to prove that he had 'executed the traitors', such was his determination to establish his position as the master terrorist of Europe.

In fact, Carlos had not the slightest idea who had given the French the details of Furoya's movements.

Nevertheless, the St. Germain des Prés outrage achieved one important purpose. It added an undercurrent of terror to the discussions going on in the cabinet not far away at the Elysée Palace, chaired by Valéry Giscard d'Estaing, President of France.

Meanwhile, the drama in the Hague continued . . .

The hostages felt that their situation was worsening. There was great anxiety about the outcome. The Japanese deliberately sharpened the atmosphere of depression by constantly referring to the May 1972 attack at Lod Airport and the September 1972 massacre of Israeli sportsmen at the Munich Olympics.

'We were threatened all the time by drawn and aimed guns,' Le Comte Jacques Chenare said later. 'They occasionally fired at some spot near us to impress on us how serious they were, and what they would do if their demands weren't answered . . . I counted perhaps twenty-five bullets fired to scare us, most at the floor or ceiling of my office. These were days of anxiety and terror. We had no food or water and little sleep. It was a horrible experience which cannot be put out of my mind.'

But for all their bravado, and the shots fired into the floor and ceiling, the three Japanese seemed to have their own anxieties. Units of army and police were standing by outside the Embassy, and sharpshooters had taken up positions on nearby buildings. One sign of their fears was that they would not let the hostages go, even under guard, to the nearby toilets. They solved the problem by placing two waste-paper bins in a corner of the Ambassador's spacious office.

While the hostages were sunk in depression and fatigue, the Japanese were constantly on the alert, thanks to an ample supply of stimulants. Meanwhile, the telephone negotiations continued.

Finally, the French government capitulated. They were prepared to meet the terrorist demands.

At this point, Yutaka Furoya, still in detention in Paris, began an ugly ploy of his own . . .

Clearly Furoya wanted to repay his jailers for the weeks he had spent in detention. He refused to accept his freedom, arguing that he did not know the Japanese who had occupied the Embassy in the Hague and that he feared for his life.

The French pleaded with him. Furoya stood his ground for hours, until they were reduced to threats. He would be well advised to accept release, they said, otherwise things would get much worse for him. But the Japanese liaison man would not give way. No, he did not know the men in the Hague, and he would not join them in Amsterdam or elsewhere.

Finally the police lost patience with him. Furoya was bundled on to a Boeing 707, clearly struggling to display his displeasure. It was a short flight to Schiphol where Furoya, playing his little game to the end, refused to leave the plane.

Eventually, at dawn on Wednesday, he joined his comrades.

When Tusiyo Umora heard that all his demands had been met, he gave the Japanese interpreter a programme for the release of the hostages. Judging from the wealth of detail, it all seemed to have been planned well in advance.

Late at night, Dutchmen sat watching the release of the hostages on their TV screens.

As they left the Embassy, the Japanese released five hostages: three men and two women. Then they climbed on a bus, together with the other six captives, including the Ambassador.

At the airport there was a temporary blackout and all routine work was stopped. As the small convoy approached, it was surrounded by dozens of army and police carriers. Snipers were in position on the rooftops, just in case the terrorists showed signs of not keeping to their agreement.

The large plane stood on a far runway. Only minutes before it had been the centre of another minor drama when the French refused to supply a crew, fearing that the airmen would only become additional hostages for the Japanese. However, at the last minute, after the Dutch prime minister had asked for volunteers, the Transavia company agreed to provide three crewmen for this hazardous flight to an unknown destination. The two Dutch pilots and an English flight engineer who agreed to take on the job showed rare courage, for they had no idea of their eventual fate or of where they might finally end up.

Television cameras followed the whole transaction.

The small bus now stood by the plane, while the other vehicles stayed well behind. Its doors opened when Yutaka Furoya approached, having finally decided to come out and prove to his colleagues that he was safe. Only then did the two hostages leave the bus, followed by a terrorist holding a levelled gun.

When the two Japanese entered the plane, the exhausted hostages were at last free to go. Minutes later, two more hostages stepped out, followed by another Japanese. They stumbled forward with the gunman prodding them in the back. Then, when their escort was aboard the aircraft, they also were allowed to go.

Now it was the turn of the Ambassador and his partner.

Chenare made a determined effort to overcome his exhaustion. He straightened up with a visible effort of will and walked with a firm stride – an immense effort by a proud and courageous man. Behind him came the last terrorist, the leader, Tusiyo Umora.

This last dramatic scene in the joint operation of Commando Boudia and the Red Army took place in half light and deathly silence.

Cameras continued to whirr, and millions sat with bated breath, watching the eerie scene. A whole world sat helpless, its eyes on Tusiyo Umora, the last of the terrorists, as he entered the cabin of the plane. Here was terror triumphant, the full weight of European civilization helpless in the face of three arch-priests of violence from another continent.

As the Boeing thundered down the runway, doctors and first-aid teams raced to the hostages. And just as the plane lifted its wheels off the ground in take-off, the lights came on again at the airport in a futile effort to brush away the nightmare of the Hague capitulation . . .

The most bitter expression of the frustration shared by millions of his fellow-men, came from the Dutch President of the European Parliament:

'Terror is not a threat to one nation. It threatens the peace of the world. To struggle against it must not add up only to lip service.'

Though senior politicians in both countries remained mute, there were strong reports in France and Holland that there was a rift. It was believed that the Dutch government had wanted to act more forcefully, to play for time until the patience and stamina of the terrorists was worn down. France's hasty, almost over-ready capitulation, had taken the wind out of the Dutch resolve to stand resolutely against the terrorists' threats.

It was a depressing display of weakness in the face of bullying threats, one more incident in a long series that seemed to prove the theories of the KGB that the Western world was morally decadent and flabby, wallowing in its materialistic preoccupations. Certainly the communists could see the justification of their elaborate plans to set up an international network and train its personnel in Moscow.

As with other such dramas in recent years, the Japanese terrorists found a haven in an Arab country. This time it was Syria. At noon on the Wednesday, the 707 landed at Damascus Airport.

Once more the Arab world was proving itself to be the firmest base for the terrorists.

CHAPTER TWENTY-FIVE

THE HUNTER RETURNS

REPORTS flowed in to Mossad headquarters from agents who gathered from various sources the unpublicized facts on the Hague siege. The details came flooding in from as far afield as Berlin, Munich, Frankfurt, Vienna, Paris, Rome, London and the Hague itself.

One point was abundantly clear. No one could supply evidence of the appearance of 'Monsieur X'. Nevertheless, agents produced data proving that Commando Boudia had prepared the groundwork for the Red Army's daring operation. A few agents had even succeeded in establishing that the head of the terror group was a man of South American or Middle Eastern appearance. This hardly sounded encouraging, since half the population of the planet could be described this way.

Only one man had not yet reported.

The Hunter.

He had vanished somewhere in Europe, doubtless diving deep into its murky waters of intrigue and subversion. That had always been his *modus operandi*, and he had obviously seen no reason to change his ways. He made no contact with any other agent, and there was no check call from him. As frustrating as this was for his chiefs, they knew that he was not a man to follow official procedures. No one dared reproach him; and they knew – or hoped – that he would surface when he felt it was time to do so.

In London, Angela Otaola was again treated to the stimulating company of her friend Carlos. In keeping with past practice, the terrorist had left the scene of his operation promptly in order to be somewhere else until things cooled down.

It was now that Carlos most appreciated his own foresight in preparing an oasis of refuge in the British capital. For the moment he had to bide his time. The Libyans were beginning to fume and fret – they were financing the Commando Boudia, but the unit seemed in no hurry to carry out Colonel Qadaffi's plans. He had wanted Arabs, not Japanese, to take the terror limelight; and he also had ideas of his own that he wanted carried out. The austere and fanatical Libyan wanted value for money, but Carlos was in no hurry to become his lackey. Taking Qadaffi's gold was one thing; becoming his tool was another.

After the efforts of recent months, some restraint was called for, as even Carlos knew. In any event, fulfilling the demands of the Libyan, which included striking at Arab leaders, would cause an open breach between the Commando Boudia and the PFLP leadership in Beirut.

This time Carlos had entered England as the Chilean Adolph Granael.

Some deep instinct had warned him against evoking his 'Hector Hippodikon' or 'Glen Everhard' identities on British soil – at least for a while.

However, his stay in London in no way incapacitated the Commando Boudia.

At Carlos's request, Michel Mukarbal stayed on in Europe to deal with the men of the unit and keep them happy with bonus rewards from the terrorist funds.

Mukarbal's attitude to Carlos was now completely revised. Their work together in preparing the Hague raid had brought Michel close to Carlos. He had learned to admire the young man, and was secretly grateful about his selection for the job in Holland, as this had given him a share in its success. Moreover, their friendship of recent months had allowed Michel to get a better look at Carlos and offered him an opportunity to appreciate the man's cultured and captivating personality. His qualities as a leader of men were now obvious to Mukarbal. And there were moments when

Mukarbal felt that his companion's analysis of operational situations, which changed by the hour, was strikingly reminiscent of the sharp and accurate interpretations of Muhamad Boudia at his best.

All in all, Michel Mukarbal was now ready to concede that there could be no better heir to Boudia's throne.

In London, Carlos was spending his time with Angela, who listened, intrigued and fascinated as always, to his stories. Now that he was back with her, she could not get enough of his company, and Carlos certainly needed no encouragement.

This period of waiting was perhaps forced upon him, but he was completely relaxed and ready to spend his time basking in Angela's loving admiration. He lolled back in her apartment, strumming his guitar, singing soft laments about love and destiny as he had once done, to other young ladies, at the Patrice Lumumba University in Moscow.

The girl clearly loved Carlos, but she did not know that he was also fostering amorous relationships with two other women who lived in nearby districts. Carlos needed women. They offered him tranquillity, escape from a more violent world. And then, again, there was something about their presence that set the spark to his imagination, sent it spiralling and soaring, sometimes to the point where reality and fantasy became inextricably entwined in his own mind.

Nancy Sanchez gave perhaps the most penetrating insight into this facet of Carlos's character. While he was away in Paris on a 'business trip', Nancy told a close friend, Angela Armstrong, an English girl who taught at the College de France:

'When he's here, everything's different. The place is full of life. Colours seem changed ... His songs, his playing ... He is an incredible mixture. He can be so many things. He is a wonderful mixture of boy and man. Sometimes he is so young you want to mother him. Then you get the feeling that there are a great many years of harsh and bitter memories of something that happened in the past. Then his face becomes hard and almost frightening ... Yes, I do love him.'

A few streets away at 11 Rue Amelie, Silvia Empara Masmala, also in love, was reading a letter from London:
'Silvia, my darling...'

While Carlos, as well as pursuing his sexual fancies, planned new and more daring acts of violence, his status was growing considerably. The other terror groups, his senior partners in the international network, had learned to admire and trust the young man who was now lying low in London. Indeed, his impressive operations, combined with excellent and close co-operation, had proved his special value to the international organization.

The crisis caused by the elimination of Muhamad Boudia was over. His young successor, the new PFLP representative in Europe, was no less a personality, and even surpassed Boudia in boldness and willingness to co-operate. After all, the release of Yutaka Furoya had been due basically to Carlos's careful and thorough preparations.

Tusiyo Umaro was full of praise. The Red Army had sent a special note of thanks to George Habash. Michel Mukarbal's report also established Carlos in the eyes of the PFLP High Command.

Many of them had been dubious, but now they were united in praising Habash for his choice of this man who had brought glory to all of them.

Oddly enough, Habash himself was the only one unimpressed by the report.

On the same shores of the Mediterranean, a little further to the South from Beirut, a plane was coming in to land at Lod Airport.

Among the crowd going through passport control was a young man of medium-height, carelessly dressed and with a briefcase in his hand. The Israeli passport that he showed to the official on duty listed him as a 'farmer'. In the vast cavern of the passenger hall, he waited patiently for his bags to come off the conveyor, and within fifteen minutes he was standing in front of a customs officer.

'Anything to declare?'

'No.'

As far as the customs man was concerned, there was nothing unusual about this young Israeli who had been away from home for several weeks. But if the young man had nothing of value to declare, he did have something valuable in his head: priceless information and a plan of action to be laid down before his superiors at Mossad headquarters.

Thanks to his contribution, the 'Adon X' file at the Mossad would no longer be as meagre as its 'Mister X' counterpart at Scotland Yard or the 'Monsieur X' dossier at the DST.

The 'Hunter' was home.

He had been away a long time, but it had been worth every minute. Roving across France, Switzerland, West Germany and Holland, he had patiently collected item after item until he reached the conclusion that he was now about to present to his chief.

On the long flight from Paris, the Hunter had carefully studied the various newspapers he had bought at Orly: *France Soir, Figaro* and others. A lot of space had been given to articles about terror and gloomy forecasts for the future. The French finally appeared to have realized that the ground was burning beneath their feet, that they were no different from other countries, and that organized terror was not willing to grant the great Republic 'privileged status' despite its constant display of sympathy for any and every Arab cause.

This was a new note – one never before detected in the French press – and the Hunter guessed that co-operation would be easier with French security agencies, smarting, as they must be, under the humiliation they had suffered at the hands of the Japanese Red Army and Commando Boudia. Help would now be extended despite the way Paris, officially at least, continued to rebuff Israel on the political and diplomatic level.

Leaving the terminal building, the young man turned towards a nearby parking lot where his own Ford Escort was waiting. Within a minute, he was driving through the main entrance to the airport.

A few minutes after three, the Hunter turned up at Mossad Headquarters.

He was greeted affectionately, and with relief, by the head of his own division. It felt comfortable to be back in familiar surroundings, particularly since the room was air-conditioned.

The Hunter started with a general resumé of his travels, without going into too many details. He knew that he would soon have to face the team responsible for the 'Adon X' file and he was holding over the detailed picture until then. He did not like repeating himself.

At 4.30 p.m., he faced five experienced men, all of whom were old acquaintances. Almost in a whisper, he began to tell of his activities in Europe. The account was precise, with no word wasted on trivia or the difficulties he had experienced. Nevertheless, his audience appreciated the complexity and thoroughness of his work. Most of what he had to say was reserved for the period following the raid on the French Embassy in Holland.

'I followed the terrorists' route twice,' he said, without giving the slightest inkling of how he had succeeded in getting on to their track. 'I was in Zurich, where the unknown met a PFLP representative and took delivery of a large sum of money. I was in Munich, where the Japanese were guests of Baader-Meinhof. I was in Paris immediately after the St. Germain de Prés bombing. And I was in the Hague.'

At this point he presented his conclusions and the data to substantiate them. Like all the other agents, he had not discovered any more details about 'Adon X'. The man was obviously very skilled and careful. But – and this was where his report differed from the others – he had identified the PFLP's liaison link: Michel Mukarbal. This Beirut-based contact-man had appeared in every one of the cities where the terrorists had set up the Hague assault.

The name was not unknown to the Mossad; there was already a file on Michel Mukarbal. It had grown very slowly, and most of the facts in it were of little real value. Consequently, he had been considered no more than a junior courier.

However, the new details brought by the Hunter aroused immediate curiosity. He was asked to repeat everything he knew about Michel Mukarbal. His description was precise and to the point. It was now clear that the terrorist was no mere minnow in a big pond. He was a key figure of far higher rank than his file indicated. And he had clearly taken part in every stage of the Red Army raid in Holland.

There was more to come.

The Hunter had noted that in at least two places Mukarbal had been seen in the company of a well-built young man who had used different names on both occasions. The general description of this unknown individual fitted with what little was known about 'Adon X', believed to be Muhamad Boudia's successor.

'My conclusion,' the Hunter said, 'is that Michel Mukarbal will lead us to the man we want.'

There was a short silence, while the members of the team sat digesting the Hunter's last comment. It was the most promising development they had stumbled on in tracking down the terrorist leader.

And it was simplicity itself.

Place a constant watch on Michel Mukarbal. Sooner or later he must re-establish contact with the unknown. The 'junior courier' was obviously the PFLP's link with the Commando Boudia, and a very important terrorist figure in his own right. The key was Mukarbal . . .

'I accept your conclusions,' the senior team member agreed. 'That is the direction we must follow. Are you prepared?'

The underlying implication of the question missed no one in the room. They all looked at the Hunter. His gaze was very steady. He seemed young and honest and calm. He slowly nodded his head.

'Yes,' he said. 'It will be my job to eliminate Adon X.'

CHAPTER TWENTY-SIX

DISASTER AT ORLY

As autumn departed new names appeared in the unrelenting Middle East conflict, now clearly affecting the rest of the world.

President Hafez el-Assad of Syria, President Anwar es-Sadat of Egypt and Prime Minister Yitzhak Rabin of Israel – who had taken over Golda Meir's job on her resignation – thrust the activities of the terrorist pace-makers off the front pages.

This was a time of negotiations. Talks between Israel and her neighbours were continuing under the baton of US Secretary of State, Henry Kissinger, who was thirsty for new successes – new blood in the arteries of a dying détente between the United States and the Soviet Union.

Behind the scenes, Arab governments were under pressure to reduce, at least for the time being, their aid to the terror organizations. Even the oil rich countries like Saudia Arabia and the Gulf States were grumbling that terrorism at the recent pitch of indiscrimination was causing unnecessary problems, as well as unease, to moderate Arab thinking.

As winter took hold, the pressure on the terrorists to restrain themselves also grew. Even Syria, known for its blind hostility to Israel, threatened the PFLP and other groups with severed relations – and a cut-off of funds – unless they showed an element of responsibility.

The terrorists were left with only one alternative: to strike at Israel on her own territory. South Lebanon, long known as 'Fatahland', was once again the doorway through which they penetrated by night, in their attempts to strike at Israel's northern settlements and civilians.

The Israeli Army stepped up its counter-terror operations.

Armoured cars moved time and time again into Fatahland, to crush pockets of would-be attackers, who dug in around and inside villages as the inhabitants, unprotected by the Lebanese army, stood helpless to stop them. Fighter planes flew overhead on strike missions against terrorist bases.

Early in December 1974, the senior officers of the Popular Front were summoned to the Lebanon. Carlos was among them. The purpose of the meeting was to impress on all the need for restraint until the Middle East situation was clearer.

Carlos rebelled against this policy of inactivity. He was now well-enough established to speak out boldly. His own victories had dazzled him. Besides, he had never forgotten that one of the major purposes of international terror, as conceived by the Russians, was to tear at the fibres of Western democracy.

The other Arab leaders agreed that there was wisdom in a temporary lull, but Carlos was not prepared to contribute to their way of thinking. Now he had a hand-picked unit of men, of whom he was just as proud as they were of him, he argued. Why not let them act? The world would tremble before their deeds.

When Habash finally lost patience and vented his spleen on Carlos in an open session, it seemed as though his authority had at last cooled the ardour of the leader of Commando Boudia. For the rest of the session he sat silent, brooding and sulky.

It was only the following day that Carlos returned to his usual high spirits, and Habash believed that he had finally seen reason and was ready to obey the new orders to keep a low profile.

After four days of consultations, the officers returned to their own centres of operations. Carlos flew to Paris. He was homesick for Nancy Sanchez and Silvia Empara Masmala.

The new terrorist champion was particularly fond of Paris in the winter, a season when the city is at its best. He enjoyed himself. The evenings were spent with Nancy's friends at 9 Rue Toullier. A warm atmosphere, a good wine, a guitar, and singing into the early hours of the morning. The Cuban girl was delighted. When Carlos was present, her parties took on a new vibrant quality of gaiety and fun.

This was the old Carlos. The singer. Carlos playing the guitar to accompany his own voice in ancient South American ballads. And there was also his undimmed talent for story-telling. Nancy radiated pleasure and it was contagious. To her friends, Carlos was that perfect mixture: a successful man-of-the-world who was also at home in the youthful atmosphere of students and those who do not have a care about the morrow.

Never for a moment did Nancy suspect that Carlos's passions and emotions were big enough to embrace many more women.

The nights and the days were pure Paris. Carlos spent hours in Nancy's company, touring the historic sites, museums and theatres.

However, there were occasions when he had to leave her for a few hours, sometimes overnight, for business meetings. Some of these stolen hours were spent with his fellow terrorists, others with Silvia at 11 Rue Amelie.

Time passed slowly for Carlos. At this stage he was not yet thinking of disobeying Habash's instructions. Commando Boudia was inactive, though scores of European agents were trying to flush its members out of their hiding places.

December was almost over.

1975 dawned, with the hint that Dr. Kissinger would succeed in bringing Israel and Egypt to another interim agreement. A first step to a hopeful peace.

For the terror organizations, the announcement was a crushing and painful blow. If, as a result of agreement, Egypt abandoned her support for small underground movements fermenting Arab violence, it would be tantamount to a dagger in the back of the Palestinian cause – or at least that was the way the frustrated terrorists viewed the situation.

The talk of peace frightened the top echelons of the different Arab groups to such an extent that they were even ready to sink their bitter rivalries and meet to discuss the best means of facing the dreaded consequences of an Egyptian 'sell-out'.

The time had clearly come for them to co-operate.

After a series of heated debates, not without their moments of deep acrimony, the Palestinian groups did agree on one thing: there would have to be a period of waiting and watching to see how the negotiations developed. Another plan they evolved – to launch strikes at Arab governments or individuals who supported an agreement – was kept a close secret.

From Habash, another message went out to his European operatives: 'Absolute inactivity until further orders.'

Once more Carlos felt frustrated. Restraint was not his strong point. He wanted action and so he looked for an outlet where his own name would once again paint lurid headlines. Indeed, he was beginning to give the impression of a man who was now becoming intoxicated with bloodlust and his own invincibility.

And it was on 10th January, 1975, that Carlos received news which prompted him to take action – and thus disobey Habash's repeated instructions to cool it.

The information was so exciting that Carlos decided not even to refer his operation to Beirut for consideration, but to put his Commando Boudia to work on the assumption that success would compensate for insubordination. The temptation of a great personal victory was too much to resist.

The details that had Carlos so excited came from a member of his commando whom he had sent to the United States to strengthen ties with pro-Palestinian groups there. He reported that Israel's Foreign Minister, Yigal Alon, then in Washington for preliminary talks about negotiations with Egypt, would be returning home between the 11th and 14th of January. The message also indicated that Alon's El Al flight would stop over at Orly for an hour.

This news was enough to jolt Carlos out of the state of inactivity forced on him against his will. He immediately asked his trusted colleague to provide precise details of flight times – for he had decided to blow up the plane during its stop-over, right on his doorstep in Paris. Alon might be killed in the attack – a blow on behalf of the Palestinians and one which would surely win him such credit that the PFLP would overlook his breach of their 'cease-fire' orders.

Success, Carlos believed, would prove to all parties that in any new political situation, the Arab Freedom Fighters remained the most potent element in the Middle East – and that among such men, Carlos was supreme.

That very same day, he began thorough preparations for the attack on the plane. He had to be exceptionally careful. Any violence in the heart of a sensitive nerve centre – as Orly clearly was – would be damaging to French prestige. Moreover, the newspapers were already linking the name of Commando Boudia with every act of sabotage on the European continent. Carlos was very much aware that hundreds of policemen and undercover agents of various nationalities were sniffing at his heels.

Nevertheless, the lure of success was too much to resist.

On 11th January, 1975, a man of about forty, dressed in a suit that spoke of excellent and expensive taste, entered a car hire office in Paris and introduced himself as a visiting businessman. He needed three cars for himself and his assistants: a Citroën GS, a Peugeot 504 and a Simca. He took the Citroën straight away, and explained, as he paid a deposit on all three vehicles, that his assistants would come by later for the other cars.

At noon, the businessman arrived at Orly Airport. Parking his car in one of the lots, he turned towards the South Terminal where El Al had its offices, and through which passengers to Israel had to pass to board their planes.

Carlos ambled in a leisurely fashion, as befitted his elegant appearance, down the long lobby of the South Terminal, through a crowd of passengers, noting the layout of the building as he went. Then he bought a one-franc ticket that allowed him on to the broad terrace overlooking the runways.

That evening, claiming that he was tired and needed a short rest, Carlos closed himself in his bedroom at 9 Rue Toullier. Locking the door, he sat down to prepare the details of his attack plan.

One by one he went over the essential points, fitting them into place in his mind.

Now all he had to do was wait for the precise information requested from the United States.

His messenger did not let him down. An El Al plane, carrying Yigal Alon, would be arriving at Orly before noon on the 12th, two days hence.

Carlos immediately sent a courier to contact the men of Commando Boudia selected for the job, summoning them to a final briefing in Nancy's apartment at 9 a.m. He knew that Nancy had a date at that time with Angela Armstrong, in a café some distance from the apartment.

El Al's Boeing 747 from New York was piloted by a veteran, Captain David Kishon, who had worked many years for the airline. Consequently, he was not particularly over-awed by the fact that a Cabinet Minister was among his passengers. For him, carrying VIP's was an almost daily event.

The flight across the Atlantic was uneventful. The giant plane approached Orly on schedule and came in to land on its usual runway, on the south side of the field. Here, it would stand an hour, load passengers, then continue to Ben Gurion Airport in Israel.

Within the hour the aircraft had been refuelled and was ready for the next leg of its journey. As it rolled slowly down the runway and revved for take-off, three men were standing on the terrace, holding two medium-sized cases. Nobody paid any particular attention to them. The weather was extremely cold and few people cared to stand on the terrace.

Since their final briefing at Nancy's apartment, the trio had remained together. There were seven in all, but the three now on the terrace had received specialist training in firing bazookas. The other four had the task of covering them.

All seven had arrived at Orly in the rented cars, the attackers in the Citroën and their back-up unit in the Peugeot. The Simca remained with Carlos, who was positioned outside the field, at a point where he could watch the runway that the El Al plane would use. All eight were in constant touch with each other by means of walkie-talkie radios.

Their intention was to hit the aircraft's fuel tank, in the hope that the resulting explosion would wipe out the Israel Foreign Minister as well as the rest of the passengers.

Visibility was excellent. There would be no problem in sighting the bazookas. By the time the plane turned on to the runway for take-off, the weapons were assembled and the range set. Then a moment of irritation. On a parallel runway, a Lebanese airliner was crossing the line of fire.

However, it was only for a moment. At exactly 12.15 the Arab plane took off, leaving the El Al Boeing once more exposed. Among the bazooka operators, the tension was growing. Luck seemed to be favouring them, for the terrace was now completely empty. Conditions were far better than Carlos had hoped for.

Orly Control Tower gave the Boeing 747 permission to take off. The giant engine thundered up to maximum thrust while the pilot held his brakes. On the ground, the flight supervisors were showing no more than normal routine interest.

At precisely 12.20 12th January, 1975, the first bazooka blasted off from the terrace. It was a ranging shot. The next two would be the killers, designed to hit the target head on. As expected, the first shell exploded close to the aircraft.

And now there arose a hitch – that unexpected element which so often lays low the plans of even the most skilled operators.

Carlos and his men knew nothing about Captain David Kishon – and the speed of his reactions stunned them.

Like most El Al captains, David Kishon had served many years as a combat pilot in the Israel Air Force. He was used to unexpected danger – and when the first shell exploded, Kishon did not even think twice: instinctively, he knew that there would be more of the same kind. In the same split second he pushed his throttle to maximum and, identifying the direction of fire, altered direction and rolled the enormous plane into shelter behind the terminal building, away from the terrace.

The Jumbo jet had just hurtled across the tarmac. Security officers, alerted by the first explosion and the sudden mad behaviour of the aircraft, were already on their way to see what had happened. The flight controllers meanwhile recovered from their initial shock and summoned emergency services – fire, rescue and ambulances – as a precaution. Shouting and frantic movement was now going on all around.

Stunned by Kishon's unexpected, lightning reactions, the attackers lost their nerve. In a panic they fired off their two remaining rockets in the wake of the rapidly disappearing Boeing. But the El Al plane had vanished from their view and the projectiles found another target instead, a Yugoslav Airlines DC9. Luckily there were neither passengers nor crew on board.

Kishon brought his plane to a halt where it was clearly no longer in danger.

And now it was the turn of the back-up men to lose their wits. Together with the three crack bazooka operators, they ran for their lives, firing their automatics wildly in all directions.

The first casualty was an airport policeman who had run on to the terrace. Although he had his gun in his hand, he seemed completely paralysed by shock as he stood watching the terrorists racing straight towards him, shooting as they came. A bullet hit him in the thigh and he fell.

Inside the terminal, panic spread everywhere. Hundreds of passengers ran in terror down the long concourse, looking for shelter. Airport employees and security men, in uniforms and plain clothes, milled around helplessly. This confusion helped the attackers forge a safe escape route, still blazing away with their weapons.

In their desperate race to get out of the terminal, Commando Boudia shot an airline stewardess and also an airport porter. Ironically, the safest and calmest place of all at the time was on board the El Al Boeing. There was no panic among the passengers – mostly Israelis returning home, and French and American tourists – because they were blissfully unaware of how close they had come to being blown to pieces.

Dumbfounded by the sheer unexpectedness of the attack, Orly security allowed Carlos's men to reach his car and get clean away without being challenged. They were soon swallowed up on the streets of the city.

Miraculously, there were only three casualties in the airport terminal, all only slightly injured, but two hours passed before some kind of calm was restored.

The Peugeot and Citroën abandoned by the fleeing terrorists were only discovered a fortnight after the abortive attack.

As always, the PFLP rushed out a statement in Beirut, lauding the men of Commando Boudia for their initiative. Yet this time there were second thoughts. On 13th January, another PFLP spokesman published a flat denial of the first announcement, saying it had clearly been made by some unknown, irresponsible force.

A number of factors combined to inspire this climbdown.

First, George Habash had forbidden any operative to act until further notice. Second, he was obviously under severe criticism from Arab governments and other terrorist groups. Finally, and most important of all, the attack had been a complete disaster.

Had his efforts been crowned with success, Carlos might have got away with a private rebuke from Habash – and much public praise in Arab circles. But failure is an orphan. Carlos was about to feel for the first time the significance of being a fighter without backing.

CHAPTER TWENTY-SEVEN

ORLY REVISITED

THREE days after the abortive attack on Orly Airport, Michel Mukarbal arrived in Paris carrying with him a stern condemnation of Carlos' behaviour.

It was a stormy session. Mukarbal felt ill at ease, for the failure had in no way reduced his admiration for Carlos. To make matters worse, the leader of Commando Boudia was in no way contrite. He cursed the PFLP command – curses that the liaison man tactfully never repeated to Habash. Now, Mukarbal tried hard to bridge the rift between his Beirut superior and Carlos, but it was useless. Carlos wouldn't budge from his determination to score a real success – and soon. But he was careful not to tell Mukarbal what he had in mind. The courier was allowed to leave with the feeling that Orly Airport was nothing more than a one-time aberration, and that he must do everything possible to soften Habash's rage.

The atmosphere in France was no less stormy. Particularly embarrassed was Foreign Minister Jacques Sauvignard. A mere twenty-fours hours before the airport incident, he had proudly announced that he was the first Western statesman to recognize the justice of the Palestinian cause and extend them the recognition 'which they deserve'. They did not deserve it now.

Both security and the pro-Arab stance of the government came under heavy attack, and the only man to stand up to the wave of criticism was Interior Minister Michel Poniatowski, who declared that the French government would in future react ruthlessly to terrorists of all kinds. He stressed the obvious: that weakness and capitulation served no purpose.

Unfortunately for him, he was speaking words that he would soon have to swallow. Within a few days he would be compelled to realize how great was the rift between high-sounding ideals and bitter reality.

In the DST a decision was taken to fight terrorism by any and every possible means. It was decided to co-operate even more closely in future with other western security services.

Carlos reacted in an extraordinary way. Failure was his Achilles heel, and he felt deeply the humiliation of having blundered. He was now like a punch-drunk boxer being hammered against the ropes and deciding to swing one wild punch, not caring that by so doing he would leave himself completely unprotected.

He paced up and down Nancy's apartment like a wild man. He was in a raging temper that lasted for days. The Cuban girl fled and, as she sat with her friends in Latin Quarter cafés, complained that her lover's business transactions seemed to have gone terribly wrong.

'Poor Carlos,' she said. 'I hope he finds a way out of his difficulties soon.'

Carlos *was* trying. But not in the way Nancy expected. In fact, he was now a man possessed . . .

A giant map of Europe was spread over a table in the Operations Room of New Scotland Yard. It was transferred to Commander Roy Habershon's office, but without its normal flags to mark the sites of the major crimes. Now the red pointers pinpointed acts of terror perpetrated by members of Terror International.

Until recently, only one area of Europe seemed relatively clear of red flags: France.

But that had changed. To the trained eye, the markers now took on the shape of an octopus, with its head in Paris.

Scotland Yard's Terror Warfare Unit was now at full stretch. The British had long ago resolved on top priority for counter-terror, and their belief that the Irish IRA were getting funds and weapons from the other groups had only strengthened that resolve. Habershon himself was always willing to co-operate with the security aims of other countries – as long as the objective remained in the field of trying to rout organized terror.

His attitude to Mossad followed the same professional thinking. The Scotland Yard man had no illusions about the nature of terrorism and violence, and he was well aware that Heathrow Airport was just as vulnerable as Orly to a band of determined men. So if Mossad needed his help in finding Commando Boudia, they were very welcome.

In answer to Israeli requests, Habershon decided to upgrade security checks at Heathrow. The same thing was happening in scores of other major cities. Certainly all agreed that as a result of such precautions, it was highly unlikely that another attack would take place. And most assuredly, the same sequence of events could not possibly occur again at any airport.

But Carlos had other ideas on the subject . . .

Four days after the bazooka attack at Orly, an Israeli agent walked into his chief's office, sat down, and asked to be sent on a mission to Europe. This was a very unusual request from the 'Hunter', who normally waited to be summoned. His superiors were therefore surprised. This was the first time he had not waited for a call.

'I really feel that I must be in Europe at a time like this,' he said, by way of explanation. 'I can't point to one fact or another, so let's just call it an instinct; but it seems to me that something is happening which is familiar from somewhere else . . .'

His voice trailed off. There was a long pause, as if he was having difficulty finding the right words, then he continued:

'Commando Boudia is controlled by the man we and others most want. But there's something in the way he operates that I recognize. It's like seeing a face in a crowd: you may never have met the man, but you're still sure you know him – and know him well.'

He glanced at his chief to see whether he was making sense. The chief's face was blank.

'Perhaps I'm not explaining myself clearly,' he added.

'I know the phenomenon,' the chief replied dryly. 'When we are frustrated, we tend to indulge in wishful thinking.'

The Hunter ignored the remark.

'No,' he said. 'This isn't wishful thinking. And I don't feel frustrated at not finding Adon X.'

'So, what is bothering you?'

'If I could explain more clearly I would,' the Hunter said. 'The problem is that I don't know exactly. I have to go and find out for myself. Nobody can do it for me. Something strange happened to me over there. Something that might be connected with current events.'

It was a bizarre conversation, unlike any the supervisor had ever experienced in his dealings with the Hunter, a man who was normally immensely practical and down-to-earth. This new dimension of mystical proportions was bothering the older man.

'Give me a few days to think about it,' he said.

The Hunter nodded and walked out without another word. His superior watched him go, uneasily. His first thought, when the Hunter had departed, was that he was dealing with a simple case of frustration at a supposed failure. On the other hand, the Hunter really did give the impression that he was on to something of importance.

It would need thinking about. Sending an agent, even one as skilled as the Hunter, purely on an instinct or emotion could prove to be dangerous.

He would think about it . . .

Sunday, 19th January, 1975. One week after the bazooka attack at Orly. An incident which no sane individual, let alone a wild-eyed terrorist, would think of repeating, in precisely the same way, detail for detail, at any airport. And, above all, not at Orly.

In the early hours of the afternoon a jumbo jet landed at the French air centre on its way from New York to Israel. On board were hundreds of tourists from the United States and Canada, as well as a sprinkling of Israelis.

Close to 4.00 p.m., the Boeing was in position at the end of the far runway, waiting for permission to take off. This was the moment that Carlos had waited for with baited breath.

The terrorist leader was having difficulty in digesting the thought that perhaps he was just not capable of commanding complex operations. Reconciliation with the idea that he was talented merely as a lone wolf was not easy. He was therefore determined to put himself to the test in the most difficult way possible. His pride demanded it, even if it meant that the lives of scores of innocent men, women and children had to be sacrificed in the process.

Thus, one week after his failure, he again stood by his car peering down the length of the runway along which the Boeing would take off.

Carlos had assumed that nobody would expect another attack, in exactly the same fashion, in Orly of all places, so soon after the first bazooka incident. It was a daring piece of devil-may-care recklessness which only a madman, or a genius, would attempt. He was determined to prove to George Habash, who had dared to criticize him, that Carlos could do anything on any scale, that Carlos was supreme among terrorists.

Certainly he possessed the ability to fire his frightened men with a new burst of enthusiasm – and was just proving that very point. His squad were convinced that the operation was of supreme importance to the PFLP, though they had no way of telling otherwise as they were not a party to High Command decisions in far-off Beirut. Their loyalty was only to Carlos.

The chief of the squad believed that the plan had to be a precise repetition of its predecessor, for security men would be thinking of other ways in which an airport could be attacked – if they were thinking along those lines at all.

So, again, there were three men on the terrace, and four were giving cover from the rear.

Amazingly, despite the first attack from the terrace, the vantage point was as unguarded as before. The bazooka team, complete with weapon and shells, gained easy accesss to the area, while the four-man back-up team also reported, to their surprise, that nothing had changed in the lax security arrangements inside the terminal building.

From his own vantage point, Carlos could distinguish nothing different from the week before. The huge plane stood at exactly the same spot. The only difference was in the hour of operation. The previous jet had left at noon. This one was due to depart at four in the afternoon. Even the skies were as clear as last time.

The Boeing began to move towards take-off point.

Then the situation changed dramatically.

At that precise moment an experienced member of the Paris Police Special Duties Squad, who was stationed below South Terminal building, thought back to the incident the week before, which had resulted in his standing there now on his normal day off. For no particular reason – as he recalled in his mind's eye how the terrorists had previously fired their bazooka from the terrace above his head – he glanced up at the very spot.

He could hardly believe his own eyes.

A terrorist was bent over a bazooka, making ready to fire at the jet now thundering down the runway.

With the reflexes of a trained marksman, the police officer pulled up his sub-machine gun and fired at the terrorist. The gun roared. Concrete exploded. The terrorist looked around and dived for cover, and the policeman kept firing.

The policeman's action stopped the attack in its tracks and probably saved the lives of hundreds of passengers. But it also opened a fresh drama which was shortly to be played out in the terminal building itself.

The three terrorists, under fire from the policeman, abandoned their attack position and beat a hasty retreat, firing indiscriminately as they moved from the terrace back into the building. Their four comrades, supposedly there to protect their rear, lost their nerve completely and fled. Policemen were now closing in on the three bazooka operators, who were retreating down the main, and very crowded, concourse.

This time, however, the police were quicker to grasp what had happened. After all, they had seen the 'same movie' – as

243

one of them later put it – the week before. Now, they began to shoot it out with the gunmen.

The terrorists, faced with resistance, lost all restraint. To clear a path through the crowd of people running frantically in all directions, they began to hurl grenades.

The noise in that enclosed space was terrifying. Explosion after explosion rocked the concourse. The screams of the wounded now added a note of hysteria to general fear and panic. People were sprawled on the floors and blood was staining the area around many of the fallen. Walls were displaying ugly blotches of crimson.

Mothers tried to protect their smaller children by pushing them to the floor and covering them with their own bodies as a shield against flying bullets and shrapnel.

Carlos's men were still looking for a way out. According to the prearranged plan, they were supposed to take hostages if trapped, and then negotiate safe passage with the authorities. Failing that, the prisoners in their hands were to be killed one by one.

The French police were still firing, and the terrorists were still retreating and hurling hand grenades to precipitate more confusion. Those who had been wounded lay where they had fallen.

Police and army units now sealed off the airport. Ambulances converged from all sides. All over the capital, hospital surgical teams were being alerted. Then, as fresh police reached the main concourse, the firing stopped.

The sight that greeted them halted the police in their tracks.

The terrorists were now shielding themselves with a group of ten hostages, among them a 70-year old man and a young woman with a baby in her arms.

There was no time to try and stop the three Arabs before they disappeared with their captives behind a toilet door . . .

It was now dark outside. Night brought a biting wind. The last wounded were carried out to ambulances, and it was soon established that twenty of them needed urgent hospitalization. Some were taken direct to operating theatres on arrival at the waiting casualty departments.

Police reinforcements were now pouring into Orly, through heavily-manned roadblocks. On the orders of the Minister of the Interior, the south end of the airport was shut down to planes. Incoming and outward bound flights were using the western runways.

Around the South Terminal a thick cordon of police stood shivering despite their overcoats. At the front of the building a room had been converted into a temporary command post for Interior Minister Poniatowski.

The habit of surrender-at-all-costs to terror blackmail had taken such a hold that nobody stopped to ask whether the French government would try to outwit the three Arabs or stand firm. Perhaps it was not the moment to ask the Minister, clearly harassed and troubled, if he intended fulfilling his commitment of resolute action, made only a few days before.

The feeling pervading the airport was that the men of violence would get what they wanted. All that mattered was: How long would the siege last?

Yet at one stage, at 8.00 p.m., French security officers gave the impression that they might make a serious attempt at storming the washrooms. An hour later, a bold Orly Police spokesman talked about the possibility of using sedation gas, but apparently nothing came of this project. The tension rose as some officers moved up to the closed doors of the toilet room, but then they retired, carrying a sheet of paper handed out through a crack in the door by one of the terrorists.

From the note, printed in French, it was learned that once again the escapade was the work of Commando Boudia.

This seemed to crack the French resolve to stand up to the terrorists, if indeed this had been their intention. Within an hour of the armed men revealing their identity, Michel Poniatowski ruled that there would be no assault. A Special Duties Squad officer explained that the decision derived from anxiety over the safety of the hostages.

To this general fear was soon added the voice of some of

the injured, interviewed by French TV. Said one man: 'Prayers must be said for the captives. There is no knowing what these devils are capable of doing.' His comment summed up the wide-spread attitude.

The tension was increased at midnight when two shots were heard from the direction of the toilets.

Under the chairmanship of President Giscard, the government endorsed the decision that further bloodshed must be avoided at all costs. The heads of the security services and police were ordered to open negotiations with the terrorists. Human life comes first, was the ruling.

However, the three armed men were in no hurry to start talking. They declined to discuss matters until eight in the morning. Their reasoning was clear: they wanted the maximum anxiety to develop over the fate of the hostages. This would strengthen their own hand.

Then, at the appointed hour, another snag arose.

The terrorists announced that they would negotiate only in Arabic, despite their fluent command of French and a number of other European languages. The Egyptian Ambassador in Paris agreed to serve as intermediary.

Among the hostages themselves, the tension was growing. They had all been locked up in washroom cubicles. As the conversation between their captors was in Arabic, they could not understand what was happening. Tiredness and fear had lowered their morale. Now they were simply waiting for something, anything, to set them free.

They were luckier than the hostages in the Hague. Negotiations were over within two hours.

Two things helped. First, the terrorists only wanted a plane and crew to take them out of France to a destination they would not reveal. Second, the French, having made their decision, were in a hurry to reach an agreement.

A Boeing 707, piloted by a French crew, was placed at their disposal. The hostages were handed over and the Air France plane began a marathon flight over the Middle East. Arab airports, one after the other, denied them landing rights.

It was an ominous sign to Carlos. It was the Arab world's

first public reaction to Commando Boudia's latest exploit. And it was not an encouraging one.

The flight lasted a wearisome and nerve-racking eight hours as the plane zig-zagged from country to country. Carlos's men were reluctant to ask Syria for permission to land, though that country was the PFLP's most enthusiastic backer. They did not want to push their luck there.

The Arab governments were clearly furious. And their anger showed as, in turn, Baghdad, Cairo, Luxor, Kuwait, Aden and Dhubai refused the aircraft permission to come to rest. Even as the plane was still airborne, the PLO terrorist organization condemned the attack:

'This incident was perpetrated as an overt blow to the good relations prevailing between France and the Palestinians, which have improved recently.'

Similar reactions came from other terror groups. And one or two Arab leaders said openly that the whole affair was aimed at hampering the United States in her negotiations with Israel and Egypt, coming as it did on the eve of President Sadat's departure from Washington.

French government officials tied themselves in strange knots to avoid public condemnation of the 'Orly Airport madmen' – as nearly everyone in the country was calling them. However, in private there was a different approach, as the Counter-Terror Branch, the DST and other security agencies were ordered to wage all-out war on Arab terror.

On the evening of 20th January, the Boeing was running out of fuel. As the sun began to set, so did the spirits of the Air France crew. One last attempt was made to secure permission to land, again at Baghdad.

Baghdad Control Tower agreed.

The second El Al jumbo jet to be saved from attack at Orly landed at Ben Gurion Airport on Sunday evening. Its crew and passengers could be thankful for their luck, but the authorities knew full well that luck does not always shine in the same direction.

At that particular moment, those responsible for Israel's security were not aware of a serious breach between the PFLP and Commando Boudia. Yet even if they had been, it would not have altered their freshly underlined resolve to open a major manhunt against all who belonged to this band.

And, in particular, 'Adon X' became the number one enemy.

Adon X had to be found.

About to be launched was the greatest manhunt ever seen in modern history. And it was not the Israelis alone who were after the blood of the Commando Boudia chief, whoever he was. There were many other countries in the search, each of whom now wanted to be the first to lay their hands on 'Mister X', 'Monsieur X' or 'Adon X'. Indeed, at that very moment similar orders were being issued to agents in England and France. Hundreds of operatives and intelligence men were again spreading out, trying to identify and then corner him.

The Hunter's request to join the chase was approved.

He had repeated his request after the second El Al incident, asking to be assigned as shadow to Michel Mukarbal, on the assumption that the courier would eventually lead him to the head of Commando Boudia. Again, he refused to spell out his strange feelings about the man's identity; all he wanted was time to check his theories against the new information he was convinced he could get.

Three days after the second raid on Orly, the Hunter was on his way. This time it would be a long route.

His first call was Paris. On the very day he arrived, a certain Ilitch Ramirez Sanchez left for London.

This was one of the few times that Carlos used his Venezuelan passport in this name. It was also the first time in his terrorist career that he felt helpless and haunted. The second failure, far worse than the first, had been an immense blow. More so because he knew that he had been so close to success on both occasions.

The personal prestige of the Commando Boudia chief now lay like a smashed pot at his feet. Two cables to Michel Mukarbal went unanswered. His attempts to reach the liaison man by phone were in vain. A wall of silence had sprung up between himself and PFLP headquarters.

Carlos was the first to disobey an order from George Habash. He was obviously also the first to do it twice running – and within the space of one week! Had he succeeded, as he knew full well, things would have been different. He would now be treading a bed of roses, not feeling isolated and disowned.

He had failed. He had failed badly.

Carlos needed to be alone. He had to get away from Paris and think about the future. He believed that he would find tranquillity in Bayswater, north of Hyde Park, in the arms of Angela Otaola.

He returned to London.

PART FIVE:

THE PHANTOM

CHAPTER TWENTY-EIGHT

A TRUE FRIEND

THE guitar lay in the corner of Angela's apartment, as neglected as a discarded mistress. Moody and depressed, Carlos sprawled for hours at a time in an old armchair by the desk. Heavy silence hung like a pall around him as the Spanish girl tip-toed about in her own home, worried and upset.

Six weeks had passed since he arrived in London. Now and again he went for long strolls in the wintry streets, but he tended to walk without seeing anything around him. He wanted to be back in action, back with the greatest narcotic he had ever known: the taste of absolute control over human life.

'Something terrible has happened to Carlos,' Angela confided to a friend in the pub where she worked.

Barry Woodhams, an amiable chemistry technician, had been courting Angela for some time. He knew Carlos, and understandably found him 'irresponsible'. He did not believe any of the stories of commercial success which had so dazzled Angela, and only hoped that this great love of her life would vanish so that she would pay more attention to his own efforts at wooing her.

'He'll bring you trouble some day,' the young man once told her, trying to exploit this unexpected situation where Angela's favourite was behaving in a less than romantic manner.

Her reply dashed his expectations.

'Who?' she said. 'Carlos? Why, he's a wonderful man! You just don't know him as well as I do. He's having a bad time right now, that's all.'

In fact, Carlos was in a quandary. The PFLP remained deaf to his efforts to contact them. He sensed that this was the end of his Commando Boudia, which he had built up so carefully and with such devotion. He might even be finished with Terror International.

One day early in March, the Spanish girl returned to her apartment to find that the rooms were all empty. On the desk she found a letter from Carlos.

'Angela, darling: I have been unexpectedly called away on business. It seems as though my affairs are taking a turn for the better. Forgive me for not being here to say good-bye. But you already know that I would have been here if possible. Don't worry, I'll be back one day soon. Yours as always, Carlos.'

She read and re-read the letter several times. She was upset, but she hoped that this trip would bring Carlos what he wanted. Then, he might return in the gay mood that she remembered with such intense pleasure.

Angela placed the letter in a bundle of others that she had received from him, from so many far-off places. Carefully she retied the ribbon around the treasured bundle and put it back in its place.

In Paris, the 'Hunter' was patiently lying in wait for Michel Mukarbal.

Mossad sources in the Lebanon had reported, at the beginning of the month, that the liaison man was planning to fly from Beirut any day. They were right. But this time there was a break from Mukarbal's long-established routine.

Mukarbal went first to London.

Henry Kissinger's shuttle diplomacy had failed a few days before. He had not brought Israel and Egypt to the table to sign a new interim agreement as he had hoped. The gap between the two parties was too wide. All the flights from Jerusalem to Cairo to Damascus and back to Jerusalem had produced nothing. Henry Kissinger, the 'magician', was left with top hat in hand and not a single rabbit.

Political drama, which had occupied news headlines for weeks, died away. But the Americans kept up the pressure.

They warned that if there was not some progress towards peace in the Middle East, another war threatened in the area. Both sides would be seriously hurt; but, far worse, war in the Middle East would surely this time engulf the whole world as the United States and Russia clashed head-on.

This talk of war put new life into the sagging morale of the terrorist movements. They wanted a new outbreak of fighting in the Middle East, for this would give them the opportunity of acting and speaking on behalf of the 'Palestinian cause'.

The new stir of activity provided an ideal opportunity for Mukarbal's private plans to mend the broken relations between Carlos and Habash. The contact man was truly fond of Carlos and admired his courage. Unlike other senior officers – and Mukarbal could name a long list of them – Carlos did not shelter behind safe stone walls in the Lebanon, seeking the prestige gained from the heroic deeds of others. Indeed, he was one of the boldest of all active commanders, and certainly the most spectacular and imaginative.

Accordingly, the moment Henry Kissinger's failure became known and the terror organizations began planning new operations, Mukarbal tried his luck with Habash. After a number of rebuffs, he finally found an attentive ear.

'The time has come to reactivate Commando Boudia,' Mukarbal said.

'Interesting idea,' Habash replied.

The taste of failure had been dulled by now. Habash was well aware that any unit which had the power of instilling such terror in the heart of Europe was of too great a value to be ignored. And sensing this change of mood, Mukarbal pressed on cautiously:

'I think it might be worth a chat with Carlos.'

'Maybe,' Habash said.

This was all that Mukarbal needed, for he knew that he had chosen his moment well. A few days earlier, a team of eight young commandos of the rival PLO had landed on Tel Aviv beach and occupied the Savoy Hotel. True, the end of the operation was less impressive than the start. An Israeli

Army unit had stormed the building at dawn on 6th March, killing all the terrorists in a short encounter – but before the Arab terrorists died, they succeeded in bringing down the front wing of the hotel on the heads of twelve guests, men and women. Hardly glorious, but the PLO was making the most of it, much to the discomfort of George Habash.

The PFLP was thus in urgent need of successes of its own – even if they ended in failure, as had the Savoy Hotel incident.

Commando Boudia was designed for just this purpose. It still existed, although dormant at the moment. All its members were totally loyal to Carlos – even if he had recently vanished as though the earth had swallowed him up.

Mukarbal did not delay. Since Carlos's last message had come from London, Mukarbal assumed that he would find Carlos there. Thus, on Wednesday, 12th March, the PFLP man arrived in the British capital. He spent a day trying to locate Carlos, but finally concluded that he must have returned to Paris. Next morning he flew on to Orly.

The Hunter was waiting for him.

The long stake-out had been worth it. At least, that is what he thought at first. He clung like a leech to Mukarbal from the moment the British Airways plane carrying his prey landed in the French capital. And this time, remembering the importance of finding 'Adon X', he was doubly careful to hide his presence from his quarry. Every few hours he changed his appearance and clothing, each time presenting a totally different image, and never letting the PFLP courier see the same shadow twice.

The Hunter stayed with Mukarbal for two days – forty-eight hours during which he never shut his eyes for fear that while he slept he would lose the vital opportunity of catching a glimpse of the man he was really after.

But Mukarbal was careful. He did not go near 9 Rue Toullier until he was sure that Carlos would be there. He phoned, but Nancy told him she had not seen her lover for some time.

The liaison man knew that Carlos was in the habit of keeping a whole harem on his string. It was therefore quite possible that he was shacked up with another young woman, unknown to Mukarbal, in some other apartment in the French capital.

Roaming through the streets of the Latin Quarter, down the alleys, around corners, through the restaurants and cafés where the PFLP men liked to congregate, Mukarbal searched high and low for his friend. Then, at the end of the second day, he decided to return to Beirut.

The search had been hopeless.

For the Hunter, this was a negative, half-time score. But, unlike Mukarbal, he decided to stay on in Paris . . .

The earth had not swallowed up Carlos. Nor was he in the arms of a woman. He was in Libya.

He had been driven to visit the oil-rich desert land in a humiliating bid to ask for yet more funds from its capricious ruler.

Earlier, Carlos had given a promise that sooner or later he would be prepared to do Colonel Qadaffi's bidding. It was a promise never kept. The money had been put to good use in consolidating his small Commando Boudia, but Carlos had shied away from the Colonel's bondage. He knew only too well that the moment he carried out a mission for Qadaffi, he would sentence himself to death. George Habash was the only man in the PFLP who had the power to negotiate with heads of State – and the terrorist leader was so jealous of this right that the whole movement would be directed at eliminating the man who had dared to serve two masters.

Frustration, however, had driven Carlos to his act of desperation. He just *had* to find funds to reactivate his loyal Commando Boudia.

On arrival at Tripoli Airport, Carlos was greeted by Habib, the Libyan-appointed treasurer of his unit. With courtesy, Qadaffi's man greeted him, inviting him for a cup of coffee in the airport restaurant. What he then said was a blow in the face to Carlos.

'I regret that I cannot help you this time. The Colonel is not interested in your services. Frankly, he no longer trusts you. And if you will take my advice, friend, don't leave this airport for Tripoli. Get on the first plane back where you came from.'

In better times this kind of talk would have sparked Carlos to cold fury, but now he was alone and abandoned. For the first time in his life he forced himself to plead: just one more chance to meet the Colonel in person, to convince him in a face-to-face discussion of the sincerity of the services offered. That was all he asked for. A chance to talk to Qadaffi.

The Libyan was doubtful, but he had a high regard for Carlos, no matter what his chief thought. Taking a chance, he drove his guest into the capital and booked him into a modest hotel. Then, clearly worried, he told Carlos:

'Wait for me here. Don't leave the hotel. I'll try, but I can promise you nothing.'

Carlos waited ... one, two, three days ... but nothing happened. Hour after hour, he paced the floor of his room, stopping occasionally by the window to look out over the city. The cries of the muezzin from Mosque minarets reminded him only to forcefully that he was in the heart of the most zealous of all Arab countries. The calls to prayer, however, only irritated him all the more as he waited ...

After five days, Habib came back. One look at the Libyan's face was enough. The Colonel was not willing to see Carlos. A man who could not keep his promise was not worthy of trust.

Carlos was ordered to leave Tripoli – and fast.

At this point he made a fateful decision. He would not return to London or Paris, but instead would head for Cyprus and from there try to make contact with George Habash. He would have to swallow his pride, but there was nothing else to do. He had gone on his knees to Qadaffi; now the process had to be repeated with the PFLP leader.

At Tripoli Airport, Carlos parted from Habib, thanking him for his efforts. In his hand he clutched a one-way ticket to Nicosia, bought with the last penny he possessed. Arriving in Cyprus at 3.00 p.m., he checked into the Olympic Hotel and headed straight for the nearest post office to send a cable to Michel Mukarbal, after having boldly borrowed some money from the hotel receptionist 'before going to the bank to change a draft'. Giving his current address, Carlos finished with the words: 'This time I expect an answer.' Down he certainly was – but not yet counted out.

Despite the fatigue and mental stress he had suffered in recent weeks, Carlos went for a stroll through the charming streets of Nicosia. He walked for hours and then, when the electric lights flickered on across the city, remembered how hungry he was.

Returning to his hotel at ten that evening, Carlos approached the reception desk to ask if there were any messages for him.

'Sorry, sir.'

It was one of the blackest moments of his life, and turning with a shrug of despair, he walked up to the first floor and then along to his room which was at the far end of the corridor. He inserted the key in the lock. Then he froze.

The door was open.

'I've been waiting for you,' Mukarbal said.

The despair and fatigue vanished from Carlos's face when he saw the man from Beirut. And the news was equally good. Habash's fury had subsided, and the opportunity was now ripe to mend fences. As Mukarbal explained frankly, nobody could deny Carlos's special value to the PFLP. Then, modestly waving aside his own role in helping to re-establish his friend's special status, Mukarbal revealed that he had also brought money, sufficient for Carlos to revive Commando Boudia and place it back on an active footing.

'Brothers also argue,' Mukarbal said with a smile. 'But blood is thicker than water.'

'I have never forgotten it,' Carlos said.

'Neither did Habash, when he was so reminded,' Mukarbal purred. 'The family remains a family. That's all that matters. We have to go on with the common cause that is so dear to us.'

Carlos was soon to understand what was meant by the 'common cause', for Habash had an outstanding ability to forecast the future and this enabled him to plan well ahead.

Instructions for future operations were now relayed to

Carlos by Mukarbal. The PFLP leader was willing to give its commander a free hand in re-training Commando Boudia and getting the men back into fighting trim. But there must be no straying from discipline; Habash would have to approve every operation from now on. After the past months, Carlos was only too happy to accept this condition.

Mukarbal then painted the operational picture that Habash had outlined. It was to lead to the peak of Carlos's fame – and certainly the courier's words enthralled his listener.

Habash, it seemed, was not a party to the joyous crowing of other groups over Kissinger's failure to bring Egypt and Israel together. He was convinced that the American Secretary of State would try again and again, until he succeeded. Without any doubt he would soon be back in the Middle East, seeking an interim settlement which would plunge a knife into the Palestinian back. Therefore, Carlos would assassinate Kissinger.

'When and where?' Carlos asked.

'I don't know,' Mukarbal admitted. 'You will have to wait for Habash to decide. It depends on political developments, and it may take a long time. You must not reactivate Commando Boudia until this plan is finalized.'

Carlos was excited. Henry Kissinger had indeed been on his list for elimination, but Carlos had never thought that he would so soon be moved up to the top.

He needed no explanation as to the significance of the assassination of the American Secretary of State. If it succeeded, it would be a major step forward for the Palestinian cause. It might even result in a major confrontation between East and West. Removal of Kissinger would also spell the end of détente for all time. The new political situation could only be to the benefit of the Palestinians.

Moreover, this bold plan would open the door to the most senior positions in the PFLP. The fact that Habash had chosen Carlos above all others was evidence enough that Carlos was still without equal in the movement. And this meeting with Mukarbal was all he needed to restore his shattered self-confidence.

Carlos was back among friends.

The two men sat until dawn, then it was time to part. Mukarbal again asked his companion to be patient, to restrain his natural exuberance. Carlos for his part asked his guest to convey his thanks and appreciation to Habash.

'You will hear from me,' Mukarbal said as he turned to the door.

'Michel ...'

It was the first time that Carlos had used the liaison man's first name during all the time they had known each other, and Michel turned slowly, with a smile of genuine pleasure on his face.

'Yes, Carlos?'

'Michel, you are a friend. A true friend ...'

Mukarbal smiled and left.

CHAPTER TWENTY-NINE

THE GHOST OF BOUDIA

THE Hunter stayed on in Europe. He moved from place to place, scratching for clues that might solve his problem. There were no fresh reports from the Lebanon about impending trips by Mukarbal to Europe. It seemed that all contact had been broken off between the PFLP and the unknown quarry.

In mid-April, 1975, the Hunter returned to Israel and demanded a green light for his 'Mukarbal Plan'. This now appeared to be the only way to check whether or not 'Adon X' was still a member of the Popular Front or whether he had in fact been eliminated by them after his two Orly failures.

From the point of view of the Mossad, identifying the head of the Commando Boudia was still a top priority. For the Hunter there was also a personal significance – one which he had not yet explained to any of his colleagues.

There was something familiar in the unknown's behaviour. After his work in Europe, the Hunter was now convinced that only one more piece, a vital one, was necessary to complete the puzzle.

He had to find the solution to the riddle, no matter how long it took. Yet, as he knew only too well, this time he would not find it so easy to convince his superiors that Mukarbal should be handled the way Yutaka Furoya had been dealt with.

On his first day back in Israel, after reporting nothing new, the Hunter raised the question of the PFLP courier. He explained that the silence of the PFLP's European network was approaching its end, that it was quite likely that Commando Boudia would be put back to work, and that the most reasonable way of preventing this would be to have Mukarbal arrested, either by the DST or by Scotland Yard.

The assumption was that Mukarbal was more than a mere courier. His function was probably to relay new plans to the network in Europe, and his arrest would throw the organization into confusion. It could be, and here the Hunter knew he was treading on delicate grounds, that the arrest of Mukarbal would force 'Adon X' to work for his release – if X was still in fact alive – and this would enable either the Hunter or other Mossad agents to get on his tail.

There was a great deal of detailed discussion before the idea was approved, but eventually the logic of the Hunter's thinking was accepted. Mossad officers compiled a file with all the new facts on Mukarbal for transfer to European security services. The recommendation was to arrest him, and it was explained to Paris that this task would probably fall to them.

The French reply was understandably cautious and laconic. 'We'll act when the time comes – if it comes.'

They had been stung once before by the Israelis when persuaded to take a terrorist courier into captivity. There had certainly been tangible results – but nothing like the full-scale siege of the French Embassy in Holland had been expected.

The Hunter was told of the French reaction.

'After the Furoya affair, they're being careful,' his superior told him. 'But don't worry. Co-operation is a one-way street. They need us, too, from time to time.'

The Hunter pressed his point.

'I believe that arresting Mukarbal will also be to their benefit,' he said. 'We must explain this to them. Again and again if necessary. We really must press them hard.'

His superior tilted his chair back and looked the Hunter straight in the eyes.

'It's also time for me to lean on you,' he said. 'Don't you think you should now tell me what's been bothering you? What's all the mystery about?'

'I haven't hidden anything from you so far,' the Hunter said. 'All I ask is that you don't try to pressure me into telling you a story that may be unfounded. I need more time.'

'All right,' the superior officer said. 'I'll wait.'

He was, in truth, a little hurt at the lack of confidence being shown in him by his operative.

'You're wrong to take offence,' the Hunter said with a slightly nervous smile, being sensitive enough to feel the tension in the room. 'If this turns out the way I fear, then it's neither a little problem nor mine alone . . .'

At the beginning of June, 1975, there were reliable reports reaching the Arab terror groups that the US Secretary of State was indeed going again to the Middle East in an attempt to reach a new interim agreement. This project would result in the Israelis returning another strip of Sinai, including the Abu Rodeis oilfields, to Egypt. Cairo in turn would pledge not to join Syria in another war against Israel. And she would cease giving unreserved support to the Palestinians.

Other items strengthened the general impression that Dr. Kissinger would succeed this time, since both the involved parties were willing to make concessions for the sake of progress.

The Palestinian terror groups were close to panic. Peace between Egypt and Israel was a major calamity – perhaps the end of all their hopes and dreams. Official spokesmen even threatened strikes against Egyptian personalities if signature of the agreement became a reality. A number of terrorist leaders openly declared that they were planning a series of sabotage actions, aimed at preventing Kissinger's shuttle diplomacy.

The decision to assassinate Henry Kissinger was activated.

Mukarbal was again ordered to Paris to give Carlos precise orders for the elimination of the American Secretary of State.

On Sunday, 15th June, 1975, an Israeli agent in Beirut reported that Michel Mukarbal had bought a ticket for a 19th June flight to Paris. The source of information was reliable. The Israeli was a clerk in the travel agency that issued the ticket. That same day the information was passed on to the DST via Jerusalem, together with a reminder of Mukarbal's special role and of the importance of detaining him. The French promised to act in accordance with the request.

The Mossad sat back to watch events, wondering how the authorities in Paris would react. DST agents could not completely evade the issue, but past experience had taught them that taking such a step might release a whole Pandora's box of evil consequences. However, after much calculating, the DST found a way of solving their dilemma while still proving their goodwill to the Mossad.

On 17th June, the French informed the Lebanese police that a terrorist known by the name of Michel Mukarbal was about to leave Beirut for Paris. The authorities in the Middle East country were asked to arrest him if he turned up at the airport for the flight to Orly on the 19th.

It was a brilliant idea – as long as the French ignored the known reticence of the Lebanese to tangle with the terror organizations.

Beirut police decided to pass the buck on to somebody else. But who? Within twenty-four hours they had found their solution. Thus, when Mukarbal did appear at the Beirut terminal, he was approached by two airport officials who asked him to accompany them while they cleared up a certain matter.

In the authorities' room, Mukarbal was informed that the Drugs Squad had no alternative but to arrest him under suspicion of smuggling narcotics to France.

It was a neat trick. The terror groups could hardly be annoyed by routine police inquiries concerning drugs, as they were well aware of the crack-down ordered by the authorities in Paris on the passage of heroin through France.

Mukarbal's arrest was duly reported to the DST that same day. And with an immense sigh of relief the French promptly informed the Israelis of this development, expressing their deep regret that they personally had not been able to detain the man as hoped.

Five days later Mossad sent another message that Mukarbal had been released, and that this time no obstacle had been placed in his way as he set off for Paris.

To the great discomfort of the DST, the information was accurate, for an hour after the unwelcome news from Jerusalem, the French authorities received a cable from the Lebanese police, confirming that they could not hold Mukarbal any longer without good reason.

Having set a trap for themselves, the DST could hardly avoid now taking the courier into custody on his arrival at Orly. Given no choice, they decided to opt for the simple role of investigators and leave the political decisions to others. They informed the office of the Minister of the Interior that they had been compelled to detain a certain Michel Mukarbal for thorough investigation.

On 24th June, 1975, Inspector Jean Herranz and his assistants waited at Orly Airport to pick up the terrorist. This they did. A few hours later, the Mossad was informed of Mukarbal's arrest.

That same evening, the Hunter was summoned to his superior. He entered the office and sat down and waited for his boss to speak.

'Mukarbal has been arrested in Paris,' the senior officer said. 'If you still feel that you should be there, the door is open . . .'

The Hunter straightened up slowly. He looked long and hard at the man across the desk.

'Yes,' he finally said. 'Of course I'll go. But . . . maybe the time has come for me to tell you something.'

There was a long pause as he carefully chose his next words.

'You remember the Boudia affair?'

His superior was surprised at the question.

'Yes, of course,' he said. 'Nor have I forgotten your part in it. Your elimination of him was perfectly executed.'

'I'm not so sure,' the Hunter said. 'I'm not sure that I eliminated Muhamad Boudia at all.'

His superior was startled. As he looked at the Hunter with an open mouth, the Hunter carefully continued:

'It is a fact that I executed *somebody*, and that I sincerely believed him to be Boudia.'

'But . . .'

'That is,' the Hunter continued, waving his superior to silence, 'I was convinced until this "Adon X" showed up at the head of the Commando named after Boudia.'

The senior officer was perplexed. The Hunter patiently explained. He went on to mention Boudia's two mistresses. Then he reconstructed the situation which had given rise to his quandary over the strange behaviour of a man who raced from one woman to another almost without pause for breath or time to recoup his lost energies.

'Maybe it's only my imagination,' the Hunter said, 'but after I blew up the Renault 16 in the Faux St. Bernard, I passed the other woman's apartment and saw a precisely similar car, a grey Renault 16, parked in Boudia's usual place.'

'You talk as if there were *two* Boudias,' the chief said.

'No,' the Hunter replied. 'I'm talking about the one and only Boudia.'

Again waving aside an intended interruption, he continued methodically:

'I think that Boudia had a double. And I simply don't know which one I eliminated. Maybe it was Boudia. Maybe it was someone else made up to look like him. It's something I now have to find out for myself. Nobody else can do it for me.'

The room was silent. Both men were lost in thought over the bizarre story. Finally the officer spoke.

'One thing isn't clear,' he said. 'Why did you only begin to think about it when Adon X came on the scene?'

'Simple,' the Hunter replied. 'I began to get the strange sensation that the unknown's behaviour and general *modus operandi* were remarkably similar to those of Muhamad Boudia. And please understand: it is only when I know for certain who I killed in Faux St. Bernard that we will be able to pinpoint who is commanding the Boudia gang.'

'You'd better go instantly,' the chief said. 'And good luck. I think you will need it.'

The Hunter got to his feet and the two men shook hands. Then, as the Hunter turned to leave, the officer stopped him.

'Why would Boudia need a double?' he asked.

The Hunter smiled.

'In his place,' he said, 'I would have done exactly the same. When you know that your enemies are waiting behind every corner – as Boudia did know – it's the only way to gain a little more time. You simply create two opposite corners, and let your enemy race from one to the other, just as I did. Basically, the hope is that the man trying to locate you will finally give himself away. And even if he doesn't expose himself – as in my case – when he *does* make his strike, there is a fifty-fifty chance that he will kill the wrong individual.'

He smiled at the officer. The officer did not smile back. There was a very long silence between them, and the Hunter finally broke it.

'And now,' he said slowly, 'I must find out precisely who it was that I blew to pieces in that street in Paris.'

CHAPTER THIRTY

MUKARBAL IS INTERROGATED

Mukarbal's arrest was kept secret. The DST decided to pump him for every piece of information that he had – with the minimum of interference from outsiders or the press. The knowledge of his arrest might spark off an act of violence from Mukarbal's comrades, but before that happened the DST were determined to get all the information they could from him.

Mukarbal was installed in an isolated room on the upper floor of DST headquarters. His interrogation was delayed by some hours while Inspector Herranz and his men examined his luggage and the documents in his brief case. Most of the papers had to do with bank accounts in Zurich and Paris, and were, on the surface, completely innocent documents. The investigators examined every word, but there were no leads for them to work on in what was to be a difficult confrontation.

That evening, Herranz decided to question Mukarbal personally. Leaving two armed guards outside the door, he entered the room to find Mukarbal reading a French newspaper. Noticing the inspector, the detained man lifted his head. Herranz waved him down.

'No need to stand up,' Herranz said.

Pulling over a chair, the inspector twisted it around and sat down with his arms folded on the back.

'How are you feeling, Monsieur Mukarbal?'

The question was politely put and Mukarbal smiled. He was utterly relaxed and sure of himself.

'I'm feeling fine,' he said. 'I lack for nothing. All I would like to know is how long you intend holding me here. And for what reason have I been brought here in the first place?'

'Your fate depends on your co-operation, Monsieur. It will depend entirely on you.'

'Ask what you want,' Mukarbal said.

'Right. Your name is Michel Mukarbal?'

'You know that. You have my passport. And I assure you, it is genuine.'

'Genuine? I wasn't even thinking of that. Do you know anything about forged passports, monsieur?'

'No,' Mukarbal said. 'Should I?'

The first hour went by in questions and answers of a relatively innocuous nature: date of birth, family history, current address and so on. Herranz appeared to be in no hurry to come to the point. Then he ordered a pot of coffee, and pouring two cups, he offered one to Mukarbal.

'Thank you,' Mukarbal said, equally polite.

'How long have you been a member of the Popular Front for the Liberation of Palestine?' Herranz suddenly asked.

'Me?' The face of the Lebanese registered complete surprise, then he laughed. 'I think somebody has fooled you, monsieur. I don't know anything about them – apart, of course, from what I read in the newspapers.'

'What do you think of the terror organizations?'

'I understand that they're fighting for a cause, but that's their business.'

'And yours?'

'I look after my own affairs.'

'And what are they?'

'I'm a diamond broker. Would you believe it?'

Herranz nodded. He pointed to a small stone in the ring he was wearing.

'How much is that worth, Monsieur Diamond-broker?'

Mukarbal studied the stone, then asked Harens to take the ring off his finger. Turning it towards the electric light bulb in the centre of the room, he looked at it for a few more seconds. He then returned it to Herranz.

'It's an alluvial stone from South Africa,' he said with a

269

smile. 'I hope you didn't pay too high a price for it.'

'Why?'

'It's faulty. There's a black spot in it.'

'You know valuable stones,' Herranz said. 'And those that are not so valuable.' Mukarbal smiled, and Herranz rushed in with his next question. 'And about Commando Boudia,' he said. 'What do you know about that?'

The suddenness of the question was intended to take Mukarbal by surprise, but obviously Mukarbal was made of sterner stuff.

'I enjoy talking to you, monsieur,' he said calmly, 'but if you were to tell me why I am under arrest, that would clarify things for me. You are posing questions on subjects about which I know nothing.'

The conversation lasted four hours. Herranz remained polite, and Mukarbal did not give an inch. At midnight the inspector broke off the session. So far he had learned nothing – except that his diamond had come from South Africa and wasn't worth very much money. He bid his prisoner a good night.

In the morning, Herranz's assistants took over the interrogation. Their approach was tougher, sometimes threatening. Mukarbal knew that he was watching the traditional 'carrot and stick' technique, but it didn't bother him. They battered away relentlessly, throughout the whole day, but he withstood every tactic and pressure.

Meanwhile, other investigators were poring over the statements in the Paris banks where, according to the documents found on him, Mukarbal had accounts. They discovered that all the monies had been blocked on Mukarbal's express instructions at the end of January 1975. More thorough examination produced the fact that large sums had been deposited in these accounts during certain periods of time. Also various sums had been drawn out, always by one Adolph Granael.

That night, Herranz again took over, with the same courtesy that had characterized the night before.

'You deposited respectable sums in your bank accounts,' he said.

'True,' Mukarbal replied. 'That's natural enough in my business.'

'Who is Adolph Granael?'

'A Chilean diamond broker,' Mukarbal said without pause. 'We worked together for a while. Up to this January, I think it was.'

'By what method?'

'The usual one – mutual trust. He supplied goods, and I transferred funds to one of my two accounts. Nothing special about that.'

'No, of course not. But why did you stop in January?'

'I think he went back to Chile. Pity.'

'What was a pity?'

'That he stopped dealing with me. I made a good profit from our transactions. I hope I have the chance again some day.'

Mukarbal would not give an inch. Even when Herranz quoted facts about his activities for and within the PFLP, he stuck to his innocent and unbreakable story.

However, this period of interrogation had actually been a strain on the detained man, for he had been quite shaken by the knowledge that the French knew so much about his role in the terrorist movement.

On the third day, Herranz suggested – at a consultation session with his own staff – that they take another look at the luggage. Perhaps they had missed something important.

Skilled DST operatives went through Mukarbal's clothes and documents with a fine toothcomb. Just as they were about to give up, one of them noticed a turned-back corner in the binding of an address book. Straightening it out carefully, he found a series of digits and then a name. Herranz took the book and read the name.

'Carlos,' he muttered. 'Carlos.'

Who, or what, was Carlos?

'What about the numbers?' his operative asked.

'Five ... seven ... seven ... five ... one,' Herranz read slowly. Then he looked up and said: 'Well, it's worth a thought. It's something we didn't have before, even if it is meaningless at the moment.'

Still clutching the address book, Herranz returned to his office. He sank into a deep armchair and gazed absently at the tell-tale corner of the book. Suddenly he burst into triumphant laughter as his men watched in amazement.

'Come on!' he exclaimed. 'I want another chat with our caged bird!'

Mukarbal was weary from constant questioning. So far there was nothing to worry about. He wasn't going to say anything he didn't want to say. As far as they were concerned, he was simply a diamond merchant and they could check that out any way they wanted.

Now he sat facing the smooth-tongued inspector as the conversation again covered polite chit-chat about the lovely summer weather and Mukarbal's health and plans for his vacation. They could just as easily have been two neighbours gossiping across the garden fence.

Suddenly, without any warning, Herranz changed. There was a cold and sharp intelligence at work as he lashed out with:

'Who is Carlos?'

Mukarbal's expression didn't change.

'Someone I met a few months ago,' he said. 'I really don't know him very well.'

'You don't know him very well?'

'No.'

'Then why is his name in your address book?'

'He owes me money. We played poker in some coffee house. He lost and promised to pay up next day. When he didn't come, I made a note of his name.'

Herranz took the address book from his pocket and thrust it under Mukarbal's nose.

'Is that a sum of money?' he asked, referring to the digits.

The prisoner examined the numbers.

'Yes,' he said. 'That's it.'

Herranz lolled back and smiled.

'What money?' he asked. 'Sterling? Dollars? Some other?'

'Francs,' Mukarbal said. 'French francs.'

'That's not a small amount,' Herranz said smoothly. 'You must be quite a poker player.'

'So they say.'

'And I say you're a damned liar!' The shouted insult hit Mukarbal like a slap across the face. This was the first time Herranz had raised his voice and it cracked like a whip. 'Look at them! Look at the numbers! Is that *money*?'

'Yes . . .'

'You're a very precise man, Monsieur Mukarbal,' Herranz said sardonically. 'You win that much and you note it down – down to the very last franc!'

Mukarbal now knew that the inspector was on to his lead.

'I make a habit of noting things like that,' he countered, struggling desperately to maintain his composure.

'I'll tell you *exactly* what it is,' Herranz retaliated, waving the book under Mukarbal's nose. 'This is no sum of money, monsieur. Not even with the numeral's reversed as they are. Let's see, shall we? Five . . . seven . . . seven . . . five . . . one . . . What do you think, monsieur?'

'I don't know what you're leading to,' Mukarbal said wearily.

'I'll *tell* you what I'm leading to,' Herranz said, leaning closer to Mukarbal and waving the book under his nose. 'Reverse these numbers, insert the periods, and you get a date. One, five, seven, seven five. One, five: the fifteenth. Seven: July. Seven, five: the year of 75. You understand, Mukarbal? The 15th July, 1975. Now what date is that?'

The blood was now pounding in the terrorist's temples. His head ached and his throat was dry. Herranz had the date that the PFLP wanted relayed to Carlos: the date Henry Kissinger was to be assassinated . . .

'I don't know,' Mukarbal whispered. 'That's your interpretation. Frankly, monsieur, I don't know what you're talking about.'

Herranz stood up abruptly and left the room. He had detected the change in the voice and attitude of the detained man. Minutes later he called five experienced men into his room and told them about the turning point in his interrogation.

'I don't know if it's serious or not,' he said. 'But we must find out who this Carlos is. The name is Spanish, maybe

South American. That kind are mostly in the Latin Quarter. Find me a few Carloses!'

The men departed Herranz took a deep breath. Now he felt the after-effects of the intense effort invested in the interrogation. The whole thing might be valueless. Perhaps Carlos was a meaningless name. In that case, the investigation would reach stalemate and he might have to release the Lebanese.

By evening, the men began to return one by one to DST headquarters. They had located seven men named Carlos in the Latin Quarter. At 8.00 p.m., Herranz strode into Mukarbal's room.

'Come!' he said. 'We are going for a tour. We are going to meet your friend Carlos.'

The few hours of peace had allowed Murkarbal a chance to take hold of himself and put his thoughts in order. He guessed that Carlos must already be aware of his arrest and would have got out of France long ago. Nothing else was conceivable ... but the inspector's self-confidence now injected a new note of worry.

The terrorist courier was allowed to change into fresh underwear and a clean shirt. Then he was handcuffed and led out to a waiting car ...

CHAPTER THIRTY-ONE

DEATH AND DISAPPEARANCE

THE tenants of 9 Rue Toullier were once again feeling irritated by the strains of a guitar and booming voices coming from the third floor apartment. There were frequent noisy parties which sometimes went on until the early hours of the morning. It was pointless complaining, as the crowds of young men and women present took not the slightest notice. So windows were closed and curtains drawn in the hope of keeping out the worst of the din.

For Carlos, this was one of the happiest and gayest periods of his life. Things had changed drastically since his Nicosia meeting with Michel Mukarbal. No more depressions. No more foul moods or outbursts of rage. Now the world was his playground.

His self-confidence restored by that meeting with Mukarbal, Carlos had returned instantly to London. To the disgust of young Barry Woodhams, now suddenly banished from her life, Angela devoted every second of her time to Carlos. This was the old Carlos, as Angela had wanted him to be. He even brought her a present from Paris: a giant sea shell on which was painted a sailing ship rocking over stormy waves.

After a few days with Angela, Carlos left again on yet another of his 'business' trips. In fact, he had things to do in Paris, since Commando Boudia had to be ready for forthcoming jobs. He would need men to replace those who had left after the Orly disaster.

Nancy Sanchez and Silvia Empara Masmala were waiting with open arms, each in her own apartment. And, most certainly, the suddenly reinvigorated terrorist knew how to keep them both happy.

The work was progressing in accordance with his objectives and priorities. A new group of enthusiastic men had been found, and their training programme was proceeding to his complete satisfaction. In fact, Carlos felt that this Commando Boudia would be better and more competent than its predecessor.

Meanwhile, he was personally studying all he needed to know about the habits and movements of the US Secretary of State. This would, again, be a one-man operation with almost no chance of failure. Such a mission, dangerous as it would be, would fully restore his star in the terrorist world.

The decision appeared to be near, Carlos sensed, when, on 18th June, Mukarbal cabled that he was planning another trip to Paris for business purposes. 'I will be delighted to see you,' were the words which gave immense pleasure to the newly-restored Commando Boudia chief. And reading between the lines of the cable, he saw a clear 'go ahead' signal.

On 27th June, 1975, in the early hours of the afternoon, Carlos returned from Orly Airport after putting Nancy aboard a flight to South America where she was to spend a short holiday with her family. That night, he was planning to entertain some friends, mostly South Americans, at Rue Toullier, before moving next day to Silvia's on Rue Amelie until Nancy returned.

The guests started to arrive about ten. An hour later all were present: four men and four girls. Wine bottles passed from hand to hand, and soon the mood became more exuberant. The guitar was in Carlos's hands, and the apartment echoed to his well-known repertoire of haunting love songs.

From time to time the host brought trays from the kitchen, loaded with sandwiches and fresh bottles.

Minutes before midnight, a DST saloon pulled up facing the house at 9 Rue Toullier. By now the officers were tired of looking across the length and breadth of the Latin Quarter for their seven Carloses. Not one of the men interviewed seemed remotely connected with Michel Mukarbal. Each man had produced flawless documents, and each firmly declared that they had never set eyes on the handcuffed man.

Though the officers were not saying anything, they were obviously depressed and disappointed. The interrogation of their prisoner had seemingly led them nowhere, and their triumph in finding that name and date in Mukarbal's notebook was evaporating into a belief that it was a blind alley.

There was only one Carlos left on their list. According to Herranz's instructions, Mukarbal remained in the car, in the custody of one of the inspector's assistants. Herran's other aide joined him. They entered the cobbled courtyard and went up the old staircase. As they reached the first floor, the sound of singing on the third floor was clearly audible. They kept climbing until they reached the third floor and they stopped at the noisy apartment.

Herranz knocked on the door. No one heard him for the noise of the party. He had to knock a few more times before someone eventually came out to greet him.

It was a broad-shouldered man of about thirty, clutching a guitar in one hand.

'I'm sorry to bother you,' Herranz said, showing his identification as a police officer.

The noise from the apartment almost drowned his words.

'Be quiet!' the guitarist called out to his guests. 'We have to greet the forces of law and order!'

The strains of another guitar died away, and the singing voices tapered off. Herranz entered the apartment, followed by his assistant.

'I'm sorry about the noise,' the guitarist said. 'I suppose the neighbours have been complaining. But it's a birthday party, officer. I regret that you have been summoned here because of a little thing like that.'

Herranz was in no hurry to correct the mistake. It was better this way. At least his own apologies would be easier – if they were necessary.

'Gentlemen, can I offer you a glass of wine?' the broad-shouldered guitarist said. 'After all, it's not every day that you celebrate the passing of one more year in a man's life.'

He was sophisticated and charming. The guitar was tossed

277

casually towards one of the girls, then he picked up a bottle of wine, poured two glasses, and offered the drinks to the police officers. Herranz refused.

'I'm on duty, monsieur. Now tell me: which one of you lives here?'

'I do,' the guitarist said nonchalantly. 'The name is Carlos Andreas Martinez. Olé!'

He put the glasses down, snatched the guitar, and strummed a few notes.

'Forgive me,' Herranz interrupted him. 'May I please see your passport, monsieur?'

'Certainly,' the guitarist said, bowing slightly.

Still carrying the guitar, Carlos walked down the narrow corridor from the living-room to the bedroom. Herranz used the absence of the guitarist to send his assistant down for Mukarbal. Probably nothing would come of it, but it had to be seen through to the end.

As the bedroom door closed behind him, Carlos's expression changed. His acting in the other room had been flawless, but now he found himself sweating.

He knew who this police officer was. Herranz of the DST. This was no routine call in answer to some complaints about the noise. Besides, the neighbours had never called the gendarmerie before, so why now? No, this was something else, something far more serious.

Standing still for a moment, Carlos forced himself to breathe normally. He picked up a shirt and mopped his brow. Then, bending down, he searched behind Nancy's shoes in the lowest drawer of the closet until he found what he was looking for.

It was a loaded gun.

Removing the safety catch, Carlos thrust the weapon into his belt, under the shirt. Only then did he pick up his passport and open the bedroom door.

In a casual manner, with a grin on his face, he returned to the salon and handed the passport to the police inspector.

Just at that moment, two of Herranz's assistants appeared in the doorway, together with Michael Mukarbal. His handcuffs had been temporarily removed.

There was only one thought in Carlos's head.

Mukarbal had betrayed him.

He reacted like lightning. The gun roared in his hand. The first bullet struck Mukarbal between the eyes. The second cut down Inspector Herranz. Then he swiftly killed the other officers, Jean Donati and Raymond Dous.

Four men lay motionless on the floor. The floor was slowly turning red with blood. Three dead. Inspector Herranz, shot through the throat, was mortally wounded.

As the echoes of the shots died away, the girls began to scream with horror and shock. Spots of blood had splashed on their faces and arms. One of them vomited. A second raced back towards the interior of the apartment. The remaining two sat transfixed, like statues, watching Carlos with glassy, frightened eyes. The four young men trembled where they were, not daring to move, hardly able to believe what they had seen.

Carlos took a few steps towards Michel Mukarbal's body. He stood for a moment or two, looking down on him.

He fired another bullet into his old friend's silent heart.

There was another glance in the direction of the dying Inspector, then, the gun still in his hand, Carlos turned and ran down the stairs.

Within seconds he was swallowed up by the darkness.

CHAPTER THIRTY-TWO

MAN OF A THOUSAND FACES

HAD the Paris authorities realized that the fugitive murderer was 'Monsieur X', the man sought by police forces of a number of countries, the hunt might have been handled differently in the early hours after the dramatic events at 9 Rue Toullier.

However, to the DST and the regular police, the murder at first seemed inexplicable and lacking in any clear motive. Inspector Herranz – alive, but only just – was quickly transferred to the operating theatre of a nearby hospital. The other bodies were left where they had fallen until the investigators were satisfied that they could be moved.

Carlos's eight guests were taken for questioning to a police station near the Rue Amelie. Carlos, meanwhile, was at number 11 of that same street, making love to Silvia. After a while, he got up and walked over to the window facing the police station. There was a buzz of unusual activity, and it would continue throughout the night.

The main problem confronting the investigators was the fact that, of the four men who could throw light on the affair, three were dead and the fourth was unconscious. And the eight dazed guests could add nothing of importance.

When police photographers had finished at the scene of the crime, other detectives set to work on the documents found in drawers and closets. Most belonged to a young woman named Nancy Sanchez, who apparently had left France the day before.

Meanwhile, the citizens of France were being given the first news of the triple killing – a crime of exceptional ferocity even for a large city like Paris. They saw on television and read in their newspapers about the remarkable marksman, apparently a South American by the name of Carlos Andreas Martinez, who had shot down the police officers in cold blood.

It was not until 8.30 the following morning that the French police began to realize what lay behind this crime, for it was at this very moment that a detective found a cheque book in the name of Carlos Andreas Martinez. On its outer cover was an address: 11 Rue Amelie.

It was right on their doorstep.

A team of five detectives was sent to the apartment in question. This time they were heavily armed and ready for action. The possibility that Carlos had sought refuge there had to be taken seriously.

There was no Carlos Andreas Martinez in sight, but they did discover a big box which he had left there. It was promptly opened – and to the amazement of the detectives, it contained a wide range of weapons. There were pistols and revolvers of various types: US Army AM 26 hand grenades, Bulgarian grenades, Czech-made ammunition, and explosives for every conceivable purpose. At the bottom of the box was a long list of French personalities and Israelis living or stationed in France. This was one of Carlos's registers of individuals singled out for execution.

By ten o'clock one thing was absolutely clear. Inspector Herranz had stumbled on no ordinary criminal. He had come across 'Monsieur X' – and he had missed trapping him. It was an error which would cost him his life, and had already cost the lives of his assistants.

From that moment, one of the biggest manhunts in history was launched. French police would join those of dozens of other countries as they sought Carlos – or, as he had become known, 'The Man With A Thousand Faces'. At noon the same day, the world was told that the chief suspect, Carlos Andreas Martinez, also known as Glen Everhard and Hector Hippodikon, was wanted by international security agencies as the head of Commando Boudia.

One Monday morning in London, the young English

chemical technician, Barry Woodhams, sat reading his morning newspaper, *The Guardian*. Casually skimming over the pages, his eyes fell on the headline about the brutal killings at 9 Rue Toullier in Paris. As he read the description of the murderer, and the name Carlos Andreas Martinez, Barry shot from his chair, swept the newspaper under his arm, and rushed to Angela Otaola's Bayswater apartment.

He arrived seconds before she was due to leave for work. Showing her the newspaper story, he insisted that she check the contents of the suitcase left with her by Carlos. At first, Angela refused pointblank, but finally, tearfully, she gave in and allowed Barry to open the valise.

The two gaped in astonishment. They were not confronted by a lot of commercial documents, but by a mobile arsenal.

The young man phoned the newspaper, and the journalist who took the call quickly contacted Scotland Yard. Experts found in the case two pistols, three grenades, loaded magazines, fingers of dynamite and a set of rubber stamps for forging passports. At the bottom was a long list of names singled out for death. Among them were Yehudi Menuhin, the violinist, and playwright John Osborne.

Now there was a positive link across the Channel. A joint team of British and French investigators was hurriedly assembled. In a hunt that would take them across the world, the detectives were assisted by experts in counter-terror from the Mossad. There were plenty of other willing hands, but first and foremost were the Germans and Japanese, who had already felt the bloody blows of Terror International.

As the security services released more and more of their data on Carlos, the image of a man who changed character and face at will won him world-wide notoriety. Like Muhamad Boudia, he was given the name of 'Bluebeard' for the way in which he used women who did not know his true identity. Also, the title of 'Red and Black' – red because of his links with the KGB who had trained him, and black because he was a terrorist killer.

Probably 'The Phantom' and 'The Man with the Thousand Faces' were the two best descriptions of Carlos as again he disappeared off the face of the earth and the security men lost all track of him.

The last person to see Carlos, before he turned up in Vienna to seize the OPEC Ministers at the end of 1975, was Nancy Sanchez's English friend, Angela Armstrong. She testified to the police that she had come face to face with him in the morning after the policemen were shot – right there in the Rue Amelie as he was leaving Silvia's apartment – just minutes before the police arrived.

The last person to receive a letter showing that Carlos was still alive was Angela Otaola. A few days after the murders in Paris she received a letter from the French capital:

'Angela, darling. To my sorrow, I had to get rid of a man who betrayed me. So please understand that I must vanish for an unknown time. But I promise you, as in the past, I will be back . . .'

At the end of the first week of investigations, a minor political drama almost led to a crisis in the relationship between France and Cuba. Three senior staff members of the Cuban Embassy – Raoul St. Roderiguez, the First Secretary; Ernest Harara Rieste, the Second Secretary, and Pardo Zamore Lara, the Cultural Attaché – were expelled. It was clear that the men were involved in dealings with Carlos, either directly or through the women in his life. In any event, it provided a powerful beam of light into the murky world of intrigue woven by the Russians and their Cuban allies in the Terror International network.

The PFLP published an emotional obituary for Michel Mukarbal: 'One of the great personalities of the Palestinian struggle.'

They ignored the man called Carlos.

Firm resolve to get Carlos, dead or alive, now marked every step taken by the DST. Mossad agents sent to France to co-operate reaped the benefits of the DST's bungling of the case. For the first time they were given almost free access to all the dossiers on terror groups in Paris, as well as those outside her borders.

The Hunter used this rare opportunity to advantage.

He asked his colleagues to get the closed DST files on Muhamad Boudia, deceased Algerian . . .

CHAPTER THIRTY-THREE

THE HUNT GOES ON ...

In mid-July 1975, the Hunter returned to Israel, loaded with a vast amount of factual material which was new to his superior. A great deal had come from his own investigations, and he spent hours reporting in detail on the complexities of the battle to locate and detain, or kill, Carlos.

It was an engrossing account. His superior listened in silence to the end.

'Okay,' his superior finally asked. 'Now just who *is* this Carlos? What was the link with Boudia?'

'Nobody knows.' The Hunter had been expecting the question, and the truth was that he was further from an answer than ever before. 'The methods of Carlos and Mu-hamad Boudia are terrifyingly similar. It's almost as if a pair of twins operated there.'

'Oh?' his superior said sceptically. 'And the facts?'

'I have some facts that can only strengthen my opinion,' the Hunter continued, 'but I can't prove them right now. One of the facts is there on the file. Both Boudia's women were investigated by the DST, and both swore that he spent his last night with her.'

'Some lover,' his superior said, even more sceptically.

'Something else is clear beyond any shadow of doubt,' the Hunter went on in his quiet way. 'After the elimination of Mahmud Hamshari, Boudia realized that he was next on the list. Therefore, to confuse any possible assassins, he made use of Carlos – a man with talents identical to his own. Carlos appeared here and there as Boudia for some months, until the day Boudia died. On that day, Boudia's car appeared to be in two different places at practically the same time. Both his mistresses swore that he spent his last night with her. Now you tell me. Which one *did* I kill?'

The two men stared at each other. The mystery was incomprehensible. The silence offered up no answers.

'You will only get that answer,' the Hunter's superior finally said, 'when Carlos is caught.'

'Yes,' the Hunter said. 'Only then.'

He stood up and walked to the door.

'I want to sleep,' he said. 'Tomorrow I will return to Paris, to go on with the hunt. Do you understand, now, why I must know the answer?'

The officer looked at him for a long time.

'Yes,' he said slowly. 'I understand.'

The Hunter left. His superior lit a cigarette. He watched the smoke rise to the ceiling. Climbing to his feet, he started to pace back and forth, mulling over what the young Israeli had said. Then, turning to the window, he watched the Hunter cross the parking lot below. A small figure. Walking gracefully and leisurely. A stubborn figure . . .

'Who *is* Carlos?' the officer muttered to himself.

THE END

THE PIRAEUS PLOT BY HARRY ARVAY

THE PIRAEUS PLOT is based on dramatic, real-life encounters between the Israeli Security Branch (SB) and the Arab terrorist organization, Black September and is the third book in a continuing series.

Four extremist Arab leaders, and their followers, had joined forces in a common cause: to kill the moderate head of the Palestine Liberation Organization, Yassir Arafat. SB Commander Max Roth knew that Arafat's safety must be ensured, and the true identity of his would-be assassins must be made known – to Arafat, to the rest of the Arab world, and to the many other interested parties. Accordingly, Itzhak, Heidi, Luke and Baruch, four skilled SB commandos, were despatched to Athens, where representatives of the four terrorist groups, and the hired killers, were foregathering . . .

0 552 10055 2   40p

THE MEIROVITZ PLAN BY HARRY ARVAY

When Boris Meirovitz, an immigrant Russian Jew, volunteered his services to the Israeli Security Branch (SB) it looked like the chance they had been waiting for – the chance to infiltrate the liaison between the Russian KGB and the Palestine Liberation Organization.

But who was this man? Where did his true affinities lie? Was he, in fact, a double agent? It was up to Max Roth and his elite team of commandos to find out – and fast. So they put

THE MEIROVITZ PLAN

into operation – a game of check and double-check in which the entire security of the Israeli SB was at risk in a high-tension race against time . . .

The Meirovitz Plan is the fourth in an exciting and dramatic series by Harry Arvay.

0 552 09895 7   40p

A SELECTED LIST OF FINE
NOVELS THAT APPEAR IN CORGI